101

Veterinary Practice Management

QUESTIONS
ANSWERED

Amanda L. Donnelly, DVM, MBA

AAHA
press

American Animal Hospital Association Press
12575 West Bayaud Avenue
Lakewood, Colorado 80228
800/252-2242 or 303/986-2800
press.AAHAnet.org

Library of Congress Cataloging-in-Publication Data

Donnelly, Amanda L.
    101 veterinary practice management questions answered / Amanda L. Donnelly.
        p. ; cm.
    Other title: One hundred one veterinary practice management questions answered
    Other title: One hundred and one veterinary practice management questions answered
    Includes bibliographical references and index.
    ISBN 978-1-58326-123-1 (pbk. : alk. paper)
    1. Veterinary medicine—Practice. I. American Animal Hospital Association. II. Title. III. Title: One hundred one veterinary practice management questions answered. IV. Title: One hundred and one veterinary practice management questions answered.
    [DNLM: 1. Practice Management—organization & administration. 2. Veterinary Medicine—organization & administration. 3. Hospitals, Animal. SF 756.4 D685z 2010]
    SF756.4.D66 2010
    636.089068—dc22
                                        2010004061

Printed in the United States of America

12   13   14   /   10   9   8   7   6   5   4   3

Book and series design by Erin Johnson Design

This book is dedicated to my
loving husband, Chris,
who supports my aspirations and
inspires me with his generosity.

CONTENTS

ACKNOWLEDGMENTS

I gratefully acknowledge the support and contributions of people who have in some way helped me write this book. To begin with, my parents, Gene and Dee Donnelly, inspired me to become a veterinarian, and I decided early on to follow that career path in my father's footsteps. My parents instilled in me a passion for client service and the human-pet bond; they taught me perseverance and gave me a great many opportunities that have helped me succeed in life.

I extend my sincere appreciation to two individuals who have helped me in my career and personal development: Sam Romano, DVM, MBA, who gave me guidance and insight when I started in management and still inspires me to learn more, and Richard Timmins, DVM, who showed me all the positive attributes of a supervisor and afforded me many opportunities to develop my skills and hone my talents.

I thank all my colleagues who have so generously shared with me their knowledge and expertise, which has helped me grow both personally and professionally. Special thanks go to Katherine Dobbs, RVT, CVPM, PHR, for her guidance in helping me with this project.

This book was made possible by the contributions of many veterinary practice managers and owners around the country, who provided me with their lists of questions about practice management. They also offered ideas and suggestions to address these challenges based on their expertise, years of experience, and in-the-trenches perspectives. Thanks go to the contributors whose names appear in the "List of Contributors" section of the book.

PREFACE

Years ago, when a veterinarian started a practice, it seemed to grow despite the skills or talents of the manager in running a business. Today, however, practices have had to adapt to a more competitive and complex marketplace, where veterinary medical care is more specialized and advanced; clients are more educated, even if their "Internet education" isn't always accurate; and client services are more sophisticated, in order to cater to pet owners seeking value for the money they spend on veterinary services. In addition, the workplace has become more diverse, with four different generations in the workforce and employees seeking more life balance.

As practices have grown, the need for stronger leadership and better human resource management has also grown. Increasingly, both strategic planning and marketing planning are viewed as essential business activities for practices to thrive. The veterinary profession may be in good shape to weather a recession, but it isn't recession-proof.

In this professional environment, managing a veterinary practice is no easy task. It requires a leader capable of navigating all the critical aspects of practice management and business development. Paying attention to financial management and key performance indicators is important to maintain and enhance profitability. Even though there is no magic formula for being a perfect manager or having the most effectively run practice, there are aspects of practice management that make all the difference in whether a practice is a financially successful business that people want to work for and clients want to visit.

This book is designed to be used by practice managers trying to find answers to practice management questions or dealing with challenges unique to their role. Whether you are a new or experienced manager, the numerous ideas and references here will help you achieve success.

You will see common themes in the answers to the questions in this book. First, you'll find recommendations for developing the practice's mission, vision, and core values. You'll notice repeated references to getting the team to focus on the vision and using core values to enhance human resource management. Businesses that do so tend to be more successful.

Second, you will realize that you need to set aside time for planning—to define business goals, set a budget, write a marketing plan, or create staff training programs and employee development plans. Practices that spend time on planning rather than just reacting to daily events are usually more profitable and develop more rewarding cultures.

Finally, to succeed with practice management, you need to want to grow and improve personally and professionally. The practice owners and managers who are most admired and respected are those who strive to improve and learn more. Their efforts are rewarded by positive cultures, productive teams, and more profitable businesses.

Despite your best efforts, there will be days when you feel that managing a successful practice is a bit overwhelming. You are not alone. And you don't have to "go it alone," either. Network with other veterinary managers and use the numerous resources in this book.

101 Veterinary Practice Management Questions Answered is intended to inspire you to keep up the good work, change when you need to change, improve where you need to improve, and always strive to become a better leader.

Amanda L. Donnelly, DVM, MBA
February 2010

1

How do I properly set an annual budget?

An annual budget needs to include expense categories for all fixed and variable expenses of the practice. Most accounting software will allow you to create an initial budget based on the prior year's expenses. When developing your budget, you can refer to veterinary publications (see the resources at the end of this chapter) to be sure your major expense categories as a percentage of revenue are consistent with industry averages and benchmarks. Your practice accountant may be able to assist in developing a budget, and you can get assistance from veterinary practice consultants as well. (See this chapter's list of resources for help finding a consultant.)

The planning process for setting a budget each year needs to start several months before your annual budget is put in place. Start by looking at trends for revenues and expenses for the past two to three years. Revenue projections for the upcoming year need to be based on prior percentage changes in growth and other anticipated factors that may affect revenues, such as the economic climate, marketing efforts, or changes in the doctor's schedule. You can calculate fixed expenses and add them to the budget, but you must estimate variable costs. Start by looking at the percentage change for each major expense category over the last several years. Then anticipate and forecast additional changes in expenses that may occur, such as new hires, benefit plan price increases, planned equipment purchases, pricing changes from vendors, salary increases, marketing expenditures, building improvements, or other practice goals.

Once you have prepared an initial budget, you may need to consider where you can cut costs and how you can increase your income to achieve the desired profit target goal for the business. Once your final budget is set, review and modify it on a monthly basis. Enter the actual values of expenditures next to the budgeted values for each expense category. Analyze any items that are over budget, and meet with the practice owners monthly or quarterly to discuss these expenses. Some items may not be a problem; for example, inventory may be high for one month if the practice took advantage of a promotion for heartworm prevention inventory. In contrast, an increase in staff compensation costs indicates that you should assess staffing needs, overtime pay, and productivity.

ⅢⅢ➡ **Do It Now**

Talk to your accountant or a consultant about using the budget feature in whatever accounting software you are using (e.g., QuickBooks®, Peachtree®) if you are not already familiar with this function.

What kind of financial reports should I look at and why?

Start by determining the financial data and key performance indicators (KPIs) you want to monitor. Then make sure you run financial reports that give you the information you want to track. Review these financial reports every month with the hospital owner so you can address any negative changes. Small changes on financial reports may not be of concern, but always carefully evaluate data so you can take action before the financial health of the practice is in jeopardy.

Assess the profit and loss (P&L) statement every month to track both revenues and expenses. Calculate expenses as a percentage of gross revenues to ensure that expenses stay in line with target ranges for each expense category. If expenses are too high, you can take steps to investigate the underlying reasons and put measures in place to better control them. The P&L statement also reports net income, which gives you a general idea of practice profitability. This can help to determine whether the practice can afford to make investments in the hospital, such as equipment purchases.

In addition to the P&L statement, you can analyze reports for key performance indicators, such as doctor production, number of transactions, new clients per month, average transaction charge, and revenue by service category. Don't forget to look at reports for accounts receivable; you are unlikely to collect on accounts that go past ninety days.

It is also a best practice to run reports that track pet owner compliance for various services and products. These reports are a good indication of how the team is doing in communicating the value of your practice's services. Once you know the current level of client compliance, you can establish specific training programs or protocols to help increase pet owner compliance rates.

How can I better understand a profit and loss statement?

The income statement, or profit and loss statement, reveals whether the business operated at a profit for a specific period of time. The statement reports revenues, subtracts expenses, shows gains and losses that result from nonoperating activities, and calculates the resulting net income. Knowing some basic accounting principles will help you better understand the hospital income statement. Consider taking a basic accounting course online or at a local community college. You can also meet with the practice's accountant, who can educate you on the details of your hospital's P&L statement.

Numerous veterinary-specific publications and seminars on financial management are available to further your education. Check those listed in the resources at the end of this chapter under the headings "Publications" and "Courses."

After you have a basic understanding of the P&L statement, confirm the practice owner's business goals and target numbers for all major expenses as a percentage of revenues. Make sure you know which specific expenses are included in each expense category on the income statement. Then review the P&L information on a monthly basis, seeking to understand how it reflects the financial health of the business. Meet every month with the hospital owner to discuss significant changes in expenses and revenues, comparing the numbers with those of the previous quarter and previous year. You can also make meaningful comparisons with published industry standards to identify areas for improvement. Look for trends in data and pay attention to net income, which reflects profitability. By doing this, you will be able to identify potential problems with finances before they get out of control.

What are the most important key performance indicators I should monitor?

The most important key performance indicators for the veterinary practice can be categorized according to financial figures, which are found on your financial statements, and nonfinancial figures, which typically are related to clients and patients and can be found on other reports that usually can be run with your computer software. With respect to financial figures, KPIs are related to either revenues or expenses. You can look at your practice's KPIs to see whether your totals are in line with industry benchmarks.

Key performance indicators for revenues include gross sales, average transaction charge, and production totals for each doctor. It is a good idea to track revenues by service category, looking at the revenue for specific services as a percentage of total revenues. It is also a good idea to monitor the following major service categories: examinations and consultations, professional services, laboratory, dentistry, surgery, diagnostic imaging, vaccinations, anesthesia, hospitalization, pharmacy, over-the-counter products, boarding, and grooming. By tracking these figures, you can better determine which services might be underutilized and how your revenues in these categories compare with those of other similar practices.

You must also track KPIs related to expenses to ensure that these expenses are reasonable. Even if revenues are significant or growing, profitability suffers when practice expenses are not controlled. The most important expenditures to track are drugs and supplies, laboratory expenses, staff payroll, benefits, doctor compensation, heartworm and flea control products, diets, and facility expenses. Look at all expenses as a percentage of revenues so you can make monthly comparisons. Also compare your totals with industry standards.

With respect to clients and pets, it is important to track KPIs, such as the number of new clients and new patients each month, by doctor, client visitation rates, the number of active clients, the number of active patients, and the number of transactions per doctor. These KPIs help you determine whether the practice is attracting a sufficient number of new clients, how often clients are bringing in their pets, and how well the practice is doing with client retention.

It is best to track KPIs on a monthly basis, comparing figures with those of the previous year and looking for trends throughout the year. If your KPIs are not in line with target goals, investigate why the numbers have changed and take steps to achieve established goals. For example, if revenues are low for a particular service category, consider whether fees are too low and whether the practice needs to do a better job marketing these services to clients.

Where can I find specific benchmarks for hospital expenses to determine whether our expenses are in line with industry standards?

Several resources are available to better understand benchmarks for specific veterinary hospital expenses. Organizations such as the American Veterinary Medical Association (AVMA), the Veterinary Hospital Managers Association (VHMA), and the American Animal Hospital Association (AAHA) publish data and benchmark reports for veterinary practices on a regular basis and provide a variety of practice management resources for veterinary practices. The National Commission on Veterinary Economic Issues (NCVEI) has online survey tools so hospitals can enter data and receive comparison reports to see how their practice compares with other similar practices, and DVM360 offers a wealth of business information for veterinary practices, including articles, videos, forms, and discussion forums. The web sites for all of these organizations are included in the resources at the end of this chapter. In addition, the consulting firm Wutchiett Tumblin and Associates publishes benchmarks every year for their Well-Managed Practices Study (see *Benchmarks* for 2008 and 2009 in the chapter resources).

A number of veterinary publications print articles every year that review various benchmarks for expenses. Subscribing to veterinary industry journals and e-newsletters is a good way to keep informed of the latest benchmarks for veterinary hospitals. You can also discuss hospital expenses with the practice's accountant, bearing in mind that he or she may not be familiar with benchmarks for the veterinary profession. Finally, veterinary consultants are available to assist practices in learning about benchmarks and deciding which action steps to take if hospital expenses are too high.

How do we better control expenses, particularly during tough economic times?

When attempting to better control expenses, focus on major expense categories. Avoid what many refer to as the "paper towel" syndrome, meaning that it doesn't make sense to try to reduce costs by counting paper towels when other expense categories amount to a much larger portion of your total expenses. Look at both fixed and variable expenses when attempting to control costs, realizing that you may have limited ability to control fixed costs.

Examine how to best control some of your major expenses. One of the largest variable expenses is inventory. To reduce inventory costs, minimize the amount of inventory on the shelf and increase inventory turnover. Work closely with vendors to make sure you are receiving the best pricing and taking advantage of discounts for paying invoices before the due date. Don't buy items in bulk just to get discounts—the value of the discounts is typically negated by the large expenditure and having inventory on the shelf for multiple months. Check with the doctors to determine whether some inventory items can be eliminated. It may not be necessary to have multiple medications on the shelf that treat the same condition. Likewise, eliminate over-the-counter products that don't sell well or can be special ordered as needed.

Staff costs are another large variable expense. Monitor payroll carefully for each pay period. Eliminate any overtime and cut back on hours when necessary. Make adjustments to hours when you notice that you are overstaffed or that staff compensation expense is exceeding your target goal. Make sure you have the best rates possible for health insurance, which is one of the largest expenditures of staff benefits.

You won't be able to change fixed costs such as rent, but you may be able to lower other fixed costs, such as advertising, and to negotiate better contracts with service providers (e.g., payroll, telephone, and lawn care). Install energy-efficient thermostats and educate the staff to be mindful of conserving energy and water. For example, you may be able to make it a policy to turn the X-ray processor on only when needed rather than leaving it on all day.

7

How do I know whether we're charging appropriately for our services?

When making decisions about fees, it is important to start by developing a pricing strategy. From a simplistic standpoint, most practice owners decide whether they want to offer lower discounted fees, to price services "middle of the road" compared with other practices, or to price services at the higher end for hospitals in their area. Once the leadership has a pricing strategy in place, it is important to look at competitive pricing because some fees are "shopped" by pet owners who may ultimately change hospitals if they feel the pricing structure is unreasonable. Ideally, pricing strategies also need to account for the cost of providing the service, demographics (areas with higher costs of living have higher fees), and the value of the services.

To get an idea of what other veterinary practices charge for a variety of services, check the list of resources at the end of this chapter. Several organizations publish veterinary fee information regularly. To learn what other practices in your area are charging for routine services, the management team can simply share information by networking with other area hospitals. Bear in mind that it is illegal to talk to other practices about fixing fees or setting them at a particular rate.

When assessing your fee schedule, don't underestimate the value of veterinary services or lose focus by worrying about what clients will pay. Clients value quality medical care and service and will pay for it within reason. Price is rarely the primary factor when pet owners choose a veterinarian or decide to keep visiting a hospital. In looking at the value of veterinary services and the need to charge appropriately, it is also important to ensure that the practice charges for all services performed. Don't neglect to charge for the use of equipment, minor service items, and veterinary technician time. Examples of service items frequently missed on invoices are the use of infusion pumps, pulse oximeters, venipuncture for blood samples, cystocentesis or ultrasound for urine collection, and topical anesthesia, as well as technician time for services such as patient care and outpatient ear cleanings.

To make sure the practice is charging appropriately for services, make fee adjustments at least annually. Some practices increase fees quarterly or biannually to avoid increasing fees all at once. Regardless of the frequency, fees must be assessed and adjusted regularly to keep pace with the cost of living and increases in hospital expenses.

What are some realistic fee margins?

The most significant factors that influence veterinary fee margins are the cost of providing the service, competitive pricing for "shopped" services such as vaccinations and sterilization surgeries, and the perceived value of services—what we think clients will pay. Some services have a relatively low profit margin because of competitive pricing, whereas other services may have a relatively high profit margin because of pricing that is value based. Some of the references at the end of this chapter will help you gain more knowledge of industry averages or benchmarks for fee margins on services and products. To determine fee margins for inventory and products, use a cost-based pricing strategy. This means looking at the cost of the inventory item (including sales tax and shipping) and then adding a percentage markup and dispensing fee when appropriate. The percentage markup varies depending on the drug or product. Markups for routine medications are often around 150 percent. For more expensive drugs, markups may be in the range of 50 to 100 percent. Preventive health care products, such as heartworm and flea control medications, usually have a markup of about 100 percent. When sending inventory items (e.g., pills or liquid medications) home with the client, add a dispensing fee. Standard dispensing fees range from $8 to $12.

To decide on fee margins for veterinary services, always consider the costs associated with the service, such as supplies and the cost of labor. This is much easier to do for services such as outside laboratory testing, which require minimal supplies and staff time. Therefore, many practices mark up laboratory fees at least 100 percent.

It is much more difficult to calculate costs associated with services such as surgery, hospitalization, and patient care. For these veterinary services, factor in doctor, technician, and assistant time, and use a value-based pricing strategy. Remember that clients are paying for the staff's and doctor's knowledge and expertise as well as time. To arrive at more realistic fee margins, it makes sense to charge by the minute, when possible, for services such as anesthesia, technician time for patient care or surgery assistance, and doctor's surgery time.

How can we lower the amount of our client discounts?

The first step to eliminating lost revenues related to client discounts is to determine why the amount of money for client discounts is high. Is it because the hospital has no discount policy in place? Is it because doctors consistently feel sorry for clients so they discount their bills? Or is it because the client wasn't given a treatment plan with associated costs, so the bill is discounted when the client complains? Who receives discounts? Once you have a better understanding of the underlying factors for hospital discounts, you can institute a plan to lower the amount of the discounts.

Be sure to establish and follow set protocols for who will receive discounts and the percentage allowed. It is advisable to offer discounts only for services because the profit margin on products in the industry is often slim. Some practices give discounts in the range of 5 to 20 percent for family members, nonpracticing veterinarians, senior citizens, military personnel, breeders, and rescue groups. If you want to lower these discounts, you may need to consider decreasing the amount of the discount or eliminating discounts for a particular group. In addition, define which family members can receive discounts: those who live with the employee or any family member? And don't forget about friends of the doctors. If the practice owner gives discounts to friends, then associate veterinarians or other team members often assume it is acceptable to give discounts to their friends also.

Make it a hospital policy as well that all clients receive a treatment plan that includes the cost of care so there are no surprises when they pay for services. If pets need additional services or care that was not included in the initial treatment plan, be sure to notify pet owners of the associated costs. When clients are kept up-to-date on fees, the practice team avoids feeling the need to discount bills just because clients are unhappy or cannot afford to pay.

Once protocols are established, the team must be held account-able to adhere to them. It is helpful to educate team members about how discounts negatively affect the financial health of the practice. Consider some level of open-book management discussion at staff meetings to help the team realize the costs associated with running a hospital and how decreased profitability can affect employee benefits and wages. It is also beneficial to give positive reinforcement to team members for the work they do and to teach them that with discounts the business is in essence saying their work is not valuable. Discuss with staff the value of the services offered so they realize there is no reason to lower fees.

If a doctor or team member continues to give discounts outside of established hospital protocols, meet with him or her individually to discuss the issue, agree on solutions to remedy the problem, and clarify consequences for failure to adhere to policies.

⫸ **Do It Now**

Prepare a memo for employees outlining who is eligible for discounts and the amount they may discount. Then discuss the memo with employees at the next staff meeting, not only to establish protocols and educate team members about client discounts, but also to remind your team that the services the hospital provides are valuable.

10

What is the best way to avoid missed charges?

There are two types of missed charges: one when a team member inadvertently fails to enter charges on a client invoice, and the other when someone purposefully fails to charge a client for services. Missed charges can be quite costly to a practice, so establish protocols to minimize the chance that charges will be overlooked. Track the occurrence of missed charges by periodically auditing files; then determine the underlying cause for the missed charges and take corrective action. Measures to address "giving away" services should differ from those taken to eliminate employee mistakes in invoicing.

Every practice's operations are somewhat different; find a protocol that works best for your team. Most hospitals find it works best to have at least two people check invoices in an effort to eliminate missed charges. For example, charges may be entered into the computer by a veterinary assistant after appointments and then double-checked against the medical record by a receptionist. For hospitalized and surgery patients, assign two members of the technical team to make sure all charges are entered. One veterinary technician can input all charges and then place the chart in a "double-check" wall box. A different technician then pulls the chart and reviews the charges before taking the record to the front desk for dismissal. In addition, it is helpful to have group service codes that include all the services for specific procedures. This saves time when entering charges and makes it less likely that the team will forget to enter some service items.

Use travel sheets to keep track of services for patients. Some practices highlight requested or anticipated services on the travel sheet and then circle items as the services are performed. Try to have two people verify the accuracy of the travel sheet and compare the charges with the medical record and treatment plans that were given to the client.

11

What is the best way to handle accounts receivable?

First, take steps to *minimize* accounts receivable. Require that all clients provide payment at the time of service. Offer a variety of payment options, third-party payment plans, pet insurance, and alternatives to costly procedures to help the client afford care. Educating clients about payment options, providing treatment plan costs, and requiring a 50 percent deposit for large invoices or for clients you don't know well will help keep accounts receivable down.

Next, establish a written credit policy so team members know if and when they can allow clients to make scheduled payments. Require clients who charge expenses to fill out a credit application and payment agreement that clearly spells out the payment arrangements. It is risky to extend credit to clients unless they are loyal, are long-standing, and have demonstrated in the past that they will pay on time.

Ensure that you have a consistent process to monitor and collect on accounts receivable. Run an accounts receivable report at least monthly, and mail statements at the same time each month. Clients who miss payments should be contacted promptly. Use a combination of telephone calls and past-due letters to remind clients of their obligation if they don't keep their accounts current. The longer accounts go unpaid, the less likely the practice will collect payment. At ninety days, include with the statement a past-due letter requesting payment within ten days. If the client still does not pay, consider sending a certified final collection letter with a copy of the transaction history, demanding payment in ten business days. This letter should threaten the use of a collection agency or attorney if payment is not received. After the final ten days have passed, the account should be turned over to a collection agency or sent to small claims court.

CHAPTER RESOURCES

Groups and Associations

American Animal Hospital Association (AHHA), www.aahanet.org. AAHA has a variety of publications and tools to help veterinary practices with financial management.

American Veterinary Medical Association (AVMA), www.avma.org. The AVMA periodically publishes a report on veterinary compensation that includes starting salary statistics.

DVM360, www.dvm360.com. This web site has a wealth of business information for veterinary practices, including articles, videos, forms, and discussion forums.

National Commission on Veterinary Economic Issues (NCVEI), www.ncvei. org. NCVEI offers a large range of benchmarking and practice management resources for those in private practice.

Veterinary Hospital Managers Association, Inc. (VHMA), www.vhma.org. VHMA offers benchmark reports for members, including a biannual compensation and benefits survey.

VetPartners, www.vetpartners.org. VetPartners is a national association of experienced veterinary consultants. You can visit their web site to find a consultant to help with many areas of practice development.

Publications

Ackerman, Lowell, DVM, DACVD, MBA, MPA, *Blackwell's Five-Minute Veterinary Practice Management Consult* (Blackwell Publishing, 2007).

American Animal Hospital Association, *Financial & Productivity Pulsepoints*, Fifth Edition (AAHA Press, 2008).

American Animal Hospital Association, *Veterinary Fee Reference*, Sixth Edition (AAHA Press, 2009).

American Veterinary Medical Association, *The AVMA Report on Veterinary Compensation* (AVMA, various dates).

Heinke, Marsha L., DVM, EA, CPA, CVPM, and John B. McCarthy, DVM, MBA, *Practice Made Perfect* (AAHA Press, 2001).

Wutchiett Tumblin and Associates and Veterinary Economics, *Benchmarks 2008: A Study of Well-Managed Practices* (Advanstar Veterinary Healthcare Communications, 2008).

Wutchiett Tumblin and Associates and Veterinary Economics, *Benchmarks 2009: A Study of Well-Managed Practices* (Advanstar Veterinary Healthcare Communications, 2009).

Courses

Veterinary Hospital Managers Association, Inc. (VHMA), www.vhma.org. VHMA
offers a Certified Veterinary Practice Manager (CVPM) certification program
that includes gaining expertise in financial management.

Veterinary Management Institute (VMI), www.aahanet.org/education/vmi.aspx.
VMI is a comprehensive, "mini-MBA" program for veterinary professionals
offered by AAHA and Purdue University. One of the four management modules is
on financial management.

Veterinary Management School Level One, www.aahanet.org/education/vms1.
aspx.

12

How do I determine salaries for various positions, such as receptionist, kennel assistant, veterinary assistant, and technician?

The primary factors to consider when determining wages or salaries for staff positions are level of experience, education or certification, skill sets, and regional differences that influence the level of competition and salary ranges for employees in your area. By taking these factors into consideration, you can establish starting wages and salary ranges for each position. To determine appropriate starting salaries and to be competitive, you will need to look at wages paid by other area veterinary hospitals and businesses. Although you can always make adjustments to these figures, it helps with recruitment efforts and the interview process to have set salary ranges.

Most practices pay more to employees who have more education, skills, or experience. Licensed technicians typically start at a higher wage than veterinary assistants because of their education and expertise. When assessing employees' levels of experience, it is helpful to focus on their skill sets rather than just the number of years of experience. A team member with many years of experience is not necessarily more qualified or more productive than an employee with fewer years of tenure. You can determine fair salaries by compensating staff based on their skills and talents as well as their productivity. If you put into place a system of paying for performance, those employees who contribute the most to the practice are rewarded with higher salaries.

Don't forget to take your budget into consideration when determining staff compensation. You should make decisions on the number of staff you can afford as well as the actual salaries you can afford to pay based on a target goal for staff expenses as a percentage of revenues. Published benchmarks and averages for staff compensation for small animal practices range from 18 to 25 percent of total income.

III➡ **Do It Now**

List all your employees for each job position (e.g., receptionist, assistant, technician) along with their current hourly wages. Put the names in order of their compensation, with the highest-paid employee at the top of the list for each category. See whether you can "justify" why each team member is paid more or less than his or her co-workers. Are your most skilled, top performers paid the most?

13

What are the best benefits to offer staff?

A good benefits package can help the practice recruit and retain the best employees. To determine the best benefits to offer staff, start by asking them what they want and which benefits are most important to them. To gain this information, you can use surveys as well as open discussions during staff meetings. In addition, stay in touch with what other veterinary practices and businesses in your area are offering to keep your benefits package competitive.

The most important benefit for many employees is health insurance. Increasingly, businesses cannot afford to cover 100 percent of premiums, but most veterinary practices currently pay 60 percent or more. Try to pay at least 50 percent of health insurance coverage to offer competitive benefits. Employees also want vision, dental, and disability insurance. Be sure to quantify the actual dollar amount of insurance benefits when communicating with employees so they understand the total value of their compensation.

In addition to insurance, the most desired benefits are typically the ability to contribute to retirement plans and paid time off. The value of retirement plans is enhanced if there is an employer match for employee contributions. Since most employees appreciate time off, the more vacation and sick days offered, the more attractive this benefit will be for team members.

Other benefits that practices likely need to offer to be competitive with other veterinary hospitals are pet benefits, continuing education (CE) stipends, uniform allowances, and membership dues. Don't forget that what staff members as a whole consider to be the best benefits can vary somewhat among individuals. Flexible schedules, time off for holidays, a fun work environment, bonus or incentive plans, educational assistance, and employee assistance programs can all be good ways to attract and retain employees.

23

Paying employees' pet health insurance for one or two pets is another benefit that can be valuable for employees and benefit the practice. Pet health insurance may give employees the ability to pay for health care, and the amount of money spent on this benefit may be lower than the amount of money that is spent by the practice on discounted services for the team.

14

What is the best method of comparing health insurance policies for the staff?

You may want to establish a good relationship with a knowledgeable insurance broker who can research your options and help you compare multiple plans and companies. These individuals can handle any insurance problems or questions that arise throughout the year, and these services don't add to the cost of the insurance. Each year, re-evaluate your insurance carrier and plans by looking at the monthly cost for the company and employees, benefit schedules, co-pay and deductible information, and practicality of use by your staff. Use a spreadsheet to compare such factors as deductibles; coinsurance; and medical, hospital, and prescription drug co-pays. In addition, check the rating of the insurance companies you are considering, and talk with current clients who use these companies. Get to know your staff and their personal health care needs so you can look for the best combination of benefits to suit your team.

Once you have decided on an insurance carrier, schedule a "lunch 'n' learn" with the staff so they can be advised of their options for plans to choose and they can ask questions. (Lunch 'n' learns are informal presentations by vendors at the customers' sites, usually over the lunch hour.) Most insurance representatives are happy to discuss plan options with the staff, giving them time to ask questions and make an educated decision. Prior to the meeting, provide team members with basic information regarding the health insurance plan options and their eligibility.

15

How do I know what the competitive salaries are in my area?

Start by looking at published salary data to determine competitive salaries for your area. You can look at various veterinary resources to determine salary ranges paid by other hospitals. Several veterinary organizations publish survey data every year or two on wages for receptionists, veterinary assistants, and veterinary technicians. This information is often reported in veterinary journal articles. General salary information for your area can also be found on the Internet for positions such as receptionist, bookkeeper, and manager. Check also the resources at the end of this chapter.

Another way to know what the competitive salaries are for your area is to network with other managers both nationally and regionally. By getting to know other practice managers, you can share this type of information and communicate about other pertinent business challenges. Attending CE seminars affords you the opportunity to talk to other managers. You can also check whether a local group of managers meets in your community.

You will often discover information about competitive salaries during employee interviews if you have each candidate fill out an application that asks for current salary. It can also be helpful to know what referral practices in your area pay because these hospitals tend to pay slightly higher wages than general practices. To attract the best employees, you may need to pay wages that are competitive with specialty and emergency referral practices.

16

What's the best way to show employees how much their benefits are worth?

Develop a handout or spreadsheet that shows each employee's total compensation as a package. Every year, give each employee an annual benefits summary. This summary should include the dollar amount of the employee's salary or wages paid, bonuses, insurance benefits, paid holidays, vacation pay, sick days, pet benefits, retirement contributions paid by the hospital, paid continuing education, membership dues, uniform allowances, the employer's share of payroll taxes, and workers' compensation payments. This breakdown includes all the costs associated with the benefits in a line-item format with a total of all the benefits at the bottom. You can also divide this total by the actual hours worked to show the employee what he or she is actually making per hour versus the regular pay rate.

Be sure to communicate this with an upbeat, positive attitude. The goal is not to make employees feel they should be indebted to the practice or that you begrudge what the business has to spend, but rather to get staff to appreciate the real value of their total compensation. Employees often have no idea of the true cost and thus the value of their benefits. Consider giving them this information on a monthly basis and at the time of reviews so they don't forget what their benefits are worth. Your payroll company can help you provide benefits summaries for employees.

Inform employees about how much the practice spends on other benefits and perks that weren't specified in their benefits summary, such as the cost of employee assistance programs, training tools, gift cards, meals, holiday parties, and entertainment. The only way employees will fully understand how much their benefits are worth is through communication (preferably written) that shows the actual amount spent for each item.

17

How do I know whether we can afford to hire an associate veterinarian?

There are no easy formulas, but there are a few factors that need to be analyzed before hiring a new associate veterinarian. Practices need to quantify the anticipated amount of revenues the associate will bring in the first year after the hire and the increase in expenses related to hiring a new doctor. In addition, you must determine whether the practice is in a positive financial position such that cash reserves and net income are sufficient to cover the increased expenses before the new doctor is productive.

Although it is difficult to forecast the amount of revenues a new associate can bring in the first year, start by assessing the current caseload to determine whether there is likely to be enough work for another doctor. Is the schedule fully booked every day? How long does it take for clients to get an appointment for routine care? Are doctors often overworked in trying to provide care for patients each day? Does the practice frequently double book to fit clients in? Do doctors and technicians consistently stay hours after the normal working day to finish caring for all the patients? To better quantify the answers to these questions, look at monthly reports to see whether the number of transactions is trending upward.

When forecasting revenue production for a new doctor, evaluate his or her level of experience and skills. Veterinarians with multiple years of experience usually are higher producers than new graduates, and it may take a new graduate longer to become productive in your practice. In addition, look at the growth opportunity in your community to assess whether you will be able to attract more new clients or offer new services, which will help increase revenues.

On the expense side, look at the associate's salary, costs for more support staff, increases in inventory and supplies, and possible increases in equipment or overhead to support the new veterinarian. The practice must be able to pay additional expenses until the doctor becomes productive enough to cover his or her salary and these related expenses. If the business has little or no cash reserves and little profitability, a new associate may jeopardize the financial health of the practice. Owners must be willing and able to afford an initial decrease in net income when hiring a new associate veterinarian.

18

How do I know what the average starting salary is for associate veterinarians?

A number of resources are available for this information. Surveys will tell you industry averages for association compensation. The AVMA, AAHA, and VHMA, as well as some practice management consultants, publish survey data every year or two. See the resources at the end of this chapter. Be aware of regional or demographic differences, which may not be represented in national survey data. You can also contact area veterinary teaching hospitals or your state veterinary medical association to ask whether they collect these data. It may be helpful to contact other veterinarians in your area as well as other parts of the country to see what salary range they offer. You can look at the cost-of-living index to adjust salaries for your area when necessary to remain competitive.

Don't forget to look at the associate's compensation as a whole package, which includes the base salary, any production pay, and the cost of any benefits to be provided. You'll also need to consider the experience, skill sets, proficiency, and job performance of the associate to determine a fair salary. For example, a new graduate who can competently perform routine surgeries, has considerable experience working in a veterinary hospital, and has specific skills or expertise may be worthy of higher compensation than a new graduate who has not yet developed these skills.

19

What are different salary options for associates, and how are production-based incentives figured?

Associate veterinarians are generally paid either a straight salary, some combination of salary plus bonus, or straight production-based compensation. Salaries are generally determined based on the experience level of the veterinarian and tend to be higher in parts of the country with higher costs of living. Compensation plans that include some type of bonus or incentive and production-based pay can be structured in a variety of ways.

Veterinarians paid on production are paid a range of 18 to 30 percent of their personal veterinary medical revenue production. Ranges for small-animal general practices are usually 18 to 23 percent, and emergency clinicians and specialists often receive compensation in the range of 24 to 28 percent of production. Earlier trends of paying associates higher than 28 percent of production have reversed in recent years. When paid on straight production, associates may receive a predetermined amount of compensation or "draw" for their regular paycheck until management can calculate the exact amount of compensation that is owed based on the doctor's monthly revenue production totals. Bonuses are typically paid to associates on a monthly or quarterly basis. Some practices pay bonuses based on the revenues generated for the preceding month or quarter, whereas others utilize an accrual system for the entire year.

When associates receive a guaranteed base salary plus a bonus, the additional bonus is usually a production-based incentive paid at the same percentages as noted above. Doctors receive a bonus once the incentive percentage of their personal revenue production exceeds the amount they need to produce in order to cover their base salary. As an example, consider the case of an associate with a base annual salary of $72,000, or $6,000 monthly, and a 20 percent production-based incentive plan. This doctor needs to produce $360,000 annually in revenues, or $30,000 per month, to "cover" his or her salary ($360,000 × 0.20 = $72,000). To receive additional compensation for the month, the doctor would need to have personal production in excess of $30,000 per month. If the veterinarian produces $40,000 in revenues in one month, for instance, he or she would receive a bonus of $2,000 for that month ($40,000 × 0.20 = $8,000; $8,000 – $6,000 of base pay = $2,000 additional compensation).

When calculating production-based pay, practices often pay different percentages of production for different revenue categories. For example, doctors may not receive any credit or compensation for such services as boarding and grooming—these services are credited to the hospital. In addition, doctors often receive a lower percentage of production for certain items such as therapeutic diets, over-the-counter products, and refill prescriptions.

 CHAPTER RESOURCES

Groups and Associations

American Animal Hospital Association (AHHA), aahanet.org/membercenter/ pp_emp_insurance.aspx. AAHA's web site provides information about employee insurance programs, including The Benefits Benchmark™ survey. AAHA also publishes a statistical book, *Compensation & Benefits*, every two years with updated data on compensation and benefits packages for owners, associate veterinarians, veterinary technicians, and other staff.

American Veterinary Medical Association (AVMA), www.avma.org. AVMA periodically publishes a report on veterinary compensation that includes starting salary statistics.

DVM360, www.dvm360.com. This web site provides information on compensation and benefits.

National Commission on Veterinary Economic Issues (NCVEI), www.ncvei. org. NCVEI offers a large range of benchmarking and practice management resources for those in private practice.

PayScale for Employers, www.Payscale.com.

Salary.com, www.salary.com.

Veterinary Employee Insurance Services, www.smarthealthplans.com/AAHA. This employee benefits firm is recommended by AAHA and works with practices to create employee benefits packages.

Veterinary Hospital Managers Association, Inc. (VHMA), www.vhma.org. VHMA offers benchmark reports for members, including a biannual compensation and benefits survey.

Publications

American Animal Hospital Association, *Compensation & Benefits*, Fifth Edition (AAHA Press, various years).

American Animal Hospital Association, *Financial & Productivity Pulsepoints*, Fifth Edition (AAHA Press, 2008).

American Veterinary Medical Association, *AVMA Report on Veterinary Compensation* (AVMA, various years).

Monheiser List, Lorraine, CPA, CVA, *Compensation Models for Owners, Associates, and Staff* (AAHA Press, 2005).

Wutchiett Tumblin and Associates and Veterinary Economics, *Benchmarks 2008: A Study of Well-Managed Practices* (Advanstar Veterinary Healthcare Communications, 2008).

20

How do I manage schedule alignment in a twenty-four-hour practice?

Effective scheduling for a twenty-four-hour practice must take into account desired staff-to-doctor ratios, patient care demands, work flow changes, client service needs, and available resources. It is up to management to control staffing costs and establish reasonable staff allocation to maximize efficiency, productivity, client service, and patient care.

Prior to making decisions about staff allocation, managers can gain valuable input from team members. Doctors and supervisors have a better understanding of staffing needs and which shifts require more staff. Typically, overnight shifts require fewer staff and weekend shifts require more. Once staffing needs have been determined, practice managers can delegate the responsibility for setting monthly schedules to supervisors and department heads. These individuals should prepare schedules at least one month in advance and handle all requests for vacation and time off. When doctors or specialists in a particular department take time off, employees on their team can be encouraged to either take time off as well or be scheduled in different services.

For ease of scheduling, it is best to establish a predefined weekly schedule with specific employees assigned to the same shift each week or the same weekly rotation. Scheduling is also easier when the practice employs mostly full-time team members. Part-time employees can then be used to fill in the gaps when more staff are needed, such as during weekend shifts or to fill in for staff on vacation.

21

How do I schedule staff accurately to accommodate practice needs without overstaffing during slow seasons and understaffing during busy times?

Start with a set schedule based on your desired staff-to-doctor ratio and reasonable staffing costs. You can look at your staff expenses on a monthly basis to know whether they are in line with industry benchmarks. Then take into account seasonal differences to modify the number of staff scheduled each month. For example, you may have different schedules for summer months and for busy holiday weekends.

Try to build flexibility into the schedule by utilizing part-time employees to cover more hours when the practice is busy. In addition, advise team members that they must submit requests for time off well in advance so you can better ensure the practice is never understaffed. You can also help ease problems with understaffing by cross-training employees to handle tasks in several areas of the hospital. For example, cross-train receptionists to prepare surgical packs when the technical team is swamped. Likewise, have technicians assist during busy times at the front desk when they may not be needed by the doctors.

To address periodic overstaffing, maximize the productivity of team members by having them work on projects or participate in training programs. Slow times are a good opportunity to make staff assignments that will help increase client visits or client compliance. For example, during slow times, team members can make client-reminder or progress-check calls, organize and develop health care program tools, or meet with doctors to learn new skills or knowledge.

If staff expenses are too high because of unanticipated overstaffing (e.g., during a sluggish economy), let the staff know that they may be asked to leave early during slow times. Ask for volunteers

who would like to go home first, and rotate who leaves early if there
are no volunteers.

⫸ **Do It Now**

For each job position, create a list of tasks for employees to do when they
have down time. Prioritize the tasks and categorize the list into tasks that can
be done quickly—for example, in less than twenty to thirty minutes—and
those that take longer. Post the lists for employees to reference when they
have free time.

22

How do I schedule meetings for our staff in a way that doesn't interfere with normal business hours and appointments?

The first step when scheduling staff meetings is to make a commitment to a set schedule and stick with the schedule unless extenuating circumstances arise. Otherwise, there will always be an excuse to miss holding staff meetings, including that the practice is too busy. Staff meetings can interfere somewhat with normal business hours and appointments. However, it is shortsighted to elect to forgo staff meetings based on the desire to book every available appointment time. The advantages of staff interaction, information sharing, and training that occur during team meetings should far outweigh the downside of not being able to schedule a few appointments.

Most practices try to determine which times are slowest for the business and schedule a one- to two-hour monthly meeting during this time slot. Some hospitals find it helpful to schedule biweekly meetings to ensure adequate time is available for staff interaction and training. The most common time for staff meetings is the lunch hour, with lunch provided for the team. To accommodate employee schedules, consider rotating the day of the week for the staff meeting so it doesn't always fall on the same person's day off. Large hospitals or twenty-four-hour referral practices sometimes schedule two staff meetings at different times to ensure they accommodate all team members.

To avoid having staff meetings disrupt the business, let clients know when a "staff training meeting" is scheduled. Clients are usually very understanding and supportive of efforts to make the practice better. Some hospitals stay open during staff meetings and assign an employee to cover the reception desk and answer phones. Other practices find it works well to put a recorded message on the phone and a sign on the door that let clients know that the hospital is closed for a team meeting or continuing education. Remember to give clients a pager or cell phone number to use if they have medical emergencies.

23

How do I make staff meetings more productive and worthwhile?

There are a number of ways to make staff meetings productive. One of the biggest keys to success is to be organized. Most practices find it works best to have a designated time slot for meetings so employees always know when there will be a staff meeting and can ask for topics to be placed on the agenda. Establish a protocol for staff to submit items for the agenda and publish the agenda prior to the meeting. It is the responsibility of managers to prioritize agenda topics to ensure that the most important issues are discussed first. Less important topics can be moved to the next staff meeting if necessary. Meetings should start and end on time—this keeps the practice running smoothly and reinforces to staff the importance of time management and accountability. Assign someone to take notes for each meeting. Meeting notes should be kept for future reference and made available for employees who missed the meeting.

Another key to making staff meetings productive is to be sure to engage team members—don't have a meeting just to be holding a meeting. Staff meetings should be used for the purpose of continuing education, review of hospital policies or protocols, brainstorming sessions to improve hospital operations or service, employee recognition, and discussion of hospital goals. Encourage staff participation during meetings and facilitate input from all employees. When problems come up, brainstorm solutions or ask the team to bring back constructive ideas to solve these problems at the next meeting. Good facilitators keep participants focused, listen to feedback, summarize the discussion, and move the team to an action plan. Always leave staff meetings with an action plan to address any issues that are brought up. Make assignments and establish deadlines for all action items.

When meetings are organized and employees have the opportunity to contribute their feedback and learn, both the meetings and employees are more productive. Team members also find staff meetings more worthwhile if they are fun and uplifting. Take a few minutes at each staff meeting to recognize employees, share fun stories, or celebrate recent successes.

24

How do I manage inventory to minimize overstock and expired product and also not run out of product?

First and foremost, each practice needs to have an employee who is responsible for managing inventory. This inventory manager is usually a technician because technicians are familiar with hospital drugs and medical supplies. Be sure the inventory manager is also detail-oriented and committed to saving the practice money. You will need to work with this employee to be sure inventory costs are kept in line with budgets and industry benchmarks.

Once you have a designated inventory manager, make sure the hospital has an established, well-organized inventory management system in place. Some practices find using a computerized inventory system helps to track products and their usage. Regardless of whether you use your practice management software or a visual inventory system, determine appropriate quantities to have on the shelf, establish reorder points and reorder quantities for all inventory items, and set a schedule for ordering.

To determine the appropriate amount of inventory to maintain on your shelf, look at the quantities used in a thirty- to sixty-day time period. Quick inventory turnover minimizes overstocking and helps keep costs down. The practice management software should be able to generate reports that detail the monthly usage of drugs and supplies. You will need to adjust quantities seasonally for some products, such as flea and tick preventives.

The next step is to set reorder points for each item. If you establish a reorder point to order when you have one month's supply of product left, you should be able to maintain inventory turnover times of thirty to sixty days. There are a number of ways to "flag" your reorder points so it is clear when the reorder point has been reached. Many practices use a colored tag or card with details about the product placed in front of the remaining quantity when the re-order point is reached. These cards are then removed and placed in a designated location for the inventory manager to use when ordering.

Inventory orders are usually placed once or twice weekly (often online) with major distributors to minimize quantities on the shelf and to increase turnover times. If the inventory manager orders on a regular schedule, the practice is unlikely to run out of products. Check expiration dates every week or two when placing orders so you can make arrangements to return product if necessary.

25

How do I ensure that inventory purchases are entered into the computer and prices are updated as necessary?

Set up a protocol for unpacking incoming inventory items and processing inventory invoices. Train staff members to check off inventory items against the invoice and verify that the invoice matches the purchase order. Invoices should then be placed in a designated location for entry into the computer software system. Assign one or two employees to enter inventory purchases and prices on the computer. Hold the staff accountable to make entries within a specific time frame; typically, this is at least weekly, to ensure that fees for inventory items are updated as price increases occur.

Establish price markups for inventory items based on regular prices and not promotion or sale prices. In addition, educate staff involved with inventory management not to enter decreased prices for dispensed inventory items because these lower costs are usually due to specials or temporary reductions. Oversight of processing for inventory purchases is a matter of quality control. Managers need to periodically check to make sure protocols are being followed. Review inventory costs and service fees tied to inventory several times a year, and adjust prices accordingly. The business needs to increase fees as needed to account for any increases in hospital drugs and supplies.

Do It Now

Check with the hospital inventory manager to verify that protocols are being followed for inventory, including updating prices in the computer. Make sure at least one other employee besides the inventory manager knows how to enter updated prices. This way, you won't get behind with price updates when the inventory manager is on vacation, out sick, or busy with other projects.

How can I implement procedures to address inventory shrinkage without damaging the trust relationship with staff?

Be open with the staff about inventory shrinkage. Educate them on how inventory shrinkage negatively affects the financial health of the practice. Communicate to the team that lower profitability means there is less money to invest in hospital improvements and employee development and compensation. Once employees recognize the need for tight inventory control, they are more likely to understand that protocols must be put in place to monitor inventory and guard against problems with shrinkage.

Verify that inventory shrinkage is due to actual shortages rather than mistakes in invoicing. Leverage the use of your inventory software to help with inventory control. Alert staff if and when inventory discrepancies occur so they appreciate the gravity of the problem and can be more conscientious to avoid errors.

Put protocols in place to track orders and maintain accurate inventory counts. Have employees or the inventory manager check inventory items off invoices when they are unpacked and reconcile the invoice with the purchase order. Keep minimal stock of products on hand and open only one bottle or box of supplies at a time. Let the staff know that there will be weekly or monthly inventory counts of products, especially items such as food, heartworm and flea control products, and over-the-counter products. Require that any employee who leaves the hospital with any product have an invoice for that item.

27

How do I get my staff to comply with the rules and regulations that are put into place for their safety?

When staff members are educated about the reasons behind safety rules and regulations, they are generally more compliant. Clearly outline all safety rules in the employee handbook and make them part of the training program for all new hires. Having written policies in place that specify a discipline policy for failure to comply with regulations helps to reinforce the importance of safety. Discuss safety rules once a month at staff meetings to remind everyone that they need to follow all established safety regulations to avoid accidents and injuries.

Encourage the team to take responsibility for safety. Form a safety committee to oversee policies and protocols, watch and report safety concerns, and present monthly safety topics. Have each staff member go through Occupational Safety and Health Administration (OSHA) training with a designated committee member or team leader. Quiz employees on each section and have them sign that they have read and understand the material presented.

If there is a safety rule infraction, bring it to the employee's attention in a positive manner with advice on how to comply with regulations. If that employee still fails to comply with policies, discuss the issue in private and make it clear that failure to abide by rules will negatively affect the employee's performance review and may result in termination.

28

How do I get into complete compliance with OSHA and stay there?

Since the amount of work required to comply with OSHA standards can be labor-intensive, assign one or more team members to be in charge of completing this process. To accomplish all the tasks necessary to bring the practice into complete OSHA compliance, set realistic goals with time lines. Enlist the assistance of employees who are willing to take on extra responsibilities, and hold them accountable for meeting deadlines. Make sure your team members have all the resources and tools they need to complete their assignments, such as web sites, workbooks, DVDs, logs, and posters.

Once all the tasks have been completed to ensure compliance with OSHA standards, a program must be in place to make sure everyone knows and complies with the standards. Most practices assign responsibility for this program to a technician. Maintaining OSHA compliance is an ongoing process. Your OSHA coordinator needs to maintain accurate records, utilize logs and/or maintenance calendars to check compliance, update material safety data sheets as needed, assist with staff training, and attend veterinary OSHA seminars when offered to keep abreast of changes and updates for compliance in the industry.

You may want to consider hiring an outside company or consultant to assist with setting up initial compliance, providing staff training, and performing annual evaluations of your compliance program. The decision to seek outside assistance depends mainly on whether you have the resources to create and maintain an effective OSHA compliance program in-house.

How can we have great medical records without it being a time-consuming chore and without getting bogged down with the process of being thorough?

First and foremost, practices must accept that keeping thorough medical records is time-consuming, but it is critically important for the continuity of care, for ensuring good communication internally and externally, and for protecting the practice from medical malpractice claims. To be more efficient in completing medical records, a number of systems can help to streamline the process.

Many of the veterinary management software programs improve the efficiency of medical records by utilizing customized templates and logs. Templates used with electronic medical records (EMRs) decrease the time needed to enter specific information for each case. Establishing a lab interface with the computer allows lab results to be transferred directly to records. For practices with paper medical records, following a consistent format when making entries and utilizing forms or stickers in records can help to streamline the amount of time spent on medical records.

Leverage staff to assist with completing and auditing medical records. Team members can enter information such as patient history, progress notes, laboratory findings, and client communications. Have employees check medical records daily for completeness before they are filed. Be sure all products are written in files and all measurements are updated in the computer. A system of checks and balances catches mistakes right away and ensures that the doctor's notes are complete.

Encourage doctors to keep medical records current throughout the day by making chart entries during breaks in their schedule. Ideally, the appointment schedule should allow some time for doctors to write their medical records. Hold doctors accountable for completing medical records within a specific time frame.

30

How do I know and follow all of the appropriate labor laws?

Since labor laws are extensive and ever changing, you must make a commitment to educate yourself and stay updated on both federal and state labor laws. Sometimes state labor laws differ from federal labor laws, so you must know the specific laws for your state. In addition to making a time commitment, utilize easily available resources to learn relevant labor laws for your practice. Once you feel comfortable with your knowledge of labor laws, make certain that your business has protocols in place to ensure full compliance with regulations.

You can start your education process by reading the wealth of information available on the web sites listed in the resources at the end of this chapter. Sign up for newsletters or e-bulletins from organizations that distribute information about changes to labor laws. Check whether any webinars or local seminars are available that you can attend to augment your knowledge.

Take advantage of outside resources to assist you when needed. Make sure you have established good working relationships with your accountant, payroll service provider, and a labor lawyer so you can ask questions when needed. In addition, veterinary consultants who specialize in human resource management may be able to assist you.

Complying with all appropriate labor laws is critical to protect the rights of employees and protect the business from adverse events such as lawsuits or penalties that can occur as a result of failure to adhere to labor laws. Make sure the employee manual outlines policies related to labor laws. Have a lawyer review your employee manual prior to distribution.

⫸ **Do It Now**

Join the Society for Human Resource Management (SHRM) to stay updated on relevant labor laws. You can also bookmark the following link to check periodically for updates to state labor laws: http://www.shrm.org/LegalIssues/StateandLocalResources/Pages/default.aspx.

 CHAPTER RESOURCES

Groups and Associations

American Animal Hospital Association (AAHA), www.aahanet.org. AAHA has a variety of publications and tools to help veterinary practices manage operations. AAHA Press also offers several products to make keeping medical records easier. Look at the AAHA store on the web site under medical records.

Safety Vet, www.safetyvet.com. Owner, Philip J. Seibert, Jr., CVT, is a consultant who works specifically with veterinary practices to help them enhance their safety programs.

Society of Human Resource Management (SHRM), www.shrm.org. This web site includes information on labor laws. SHRM sends out an e-newsletter to members with updates regarding labor laws.

Stericycle, www.stericycle.com/OSHA-compliance-training.html.

US Department of Labor Occupational Safety and Health Administration, www.osha.gov; see also www.dol.gov.

Veterinary Emergency & Specialty Practice Association (VESPA), www.VESPAssociation.org. VESPA is an excellent resource for referral practices.

Veterinary Hospital Managers Association, www.vhma.org.

VetPartners, www.vetpartners.org. VetPartners is a national association whose membership includes experienced veterinary consultants. You can visit their web site to find a consultant to help you with operations management.

WhenToWork.com, www.whentowork.com. This is an online scheduling program that some managers have found to be helpful.

Publications

Ackerman, Lowell, DVM, DACVD, MBA, MPA, *Blackwell's Five-Minute Veterinary Practice Management Consult* (Blackwell Publishing, 2007).

Seibert, Philip J., Jr., CVT, *Be Safe! Manager's Guide to Veterinary Workplace Safety* (AAHA Press, 2007).

Seibert, Philip J., Jr., CVT, *Be Safe! Veterinary Safety Training for the Medical and Technical Staff* and *Be Safe! Veterinary Safety Training for the Whole Practice Team* (AAHA Press, 2007).

31

Where can I find well-qualified, high-quality support staff?

The best approach to find qualified support staff is to utilize a number of resources, including both online and print advertising as well as community contacts. Be sure to tailor your recruiting efforts for the position you need to fill. You may use different contacts and advertising sites depending on whether you are recruiting veterinary assistants, technicians, or client service representatives.

Although advertising in the local newspaper is still a valid option, most job seekers—especially younger job candidates—primarily use Internet sites when searching for a job. Monster.com is one of the best online sites for advertising. Be sure to use keywords to narrow your focus. Another web site commonly used by managers looking for receptionists and veterinary assistants is Craigslist.org/about/ sites. The following additional web sites are commonly used in the veterinary industry for listing job postings:

- Animal Health Jobs, www.animalhealthjobs.com
- AnimalJobs.com, www.animaljobs.com
- CareerBuilder.com, www.careerbuilder.com
- CareerSniff, www.careersniff.com
- DVM360, www.dvm360.com
- iHireVeterinary, www.ihireveterinary.com
- JobConnect.com, www.jobconnect.com
- National Association of Veterinary Technicians in America, www.navta.net
- Veterinary Career Network, www.veterinarycareernetwork.com
- Veterinary Information Network, www.vin.com
- Veterinary Support Personnel Network, www.vspn.org

For licensed veterinary technicians, it is best to target your advertisements to specific locations, such as area veterinary technology colleges, professional journals and web sites routinely accessed by technicians, and local or regional veterinary medical associations. If there is a veterinary technology college in your area, develop a relationship with the faculty. Instructors are usually eager to help their students find good jobs. Building rapport often helps position you as a preferred hospital for students to do their internships. Accepting interns affords you the opportunity to assess potential job candidates.

In addition to advertising, it is helpful to network with business colleagues in your community. Networking with other practice managers is valuable and may be helpful with recruiting if you agree to refer job candidates to each other when you aren't hiring. Develop contacts with local community colleges, high school counselors, hiring agencies, or your local Chamber of Commerce so you can let these people know when you have a job opening. Carry business cards at all times; you never know when you might meet someone who you think could be an asset to your team.

32

How do we position ourselves as an "employer of choice" and maintain this status?

First of all, high pay is not generally what keeps employees in the veterinary profession, but you still must have a competitive salary and benefits package to be an "employer of choice" and retain team members. Aside from compensation, the most effective way to position your practice as the best place to work is to create a positive culture. When recruiting employees, highlight specific aspects of your compensation package and culture that make the practice an attractive place to work.

With respect to salaries and benefits, stay current on competitive wages for your area. Make sure employees and job candidates understand the actual value of all their benefits in case they are considering employment elsewhere. The most preferred benefits are medical insurance, dental and vision insurance, and retirement accounts such as a 401(k) plan. If you offer additional benefits, such as flexible scheduling, a higher-than-average number of personal days, employee assistance programs, CE assistance, membership dues, uniform allowances, or pet insurance, be sure to emphasize these.

Many aspects of culture determine whether employees view the practice as a preferred place to work. First, hospitals that offer exemplary medical care and client services are seen as good places to work because most individuals want to be proud of the services offered by the practice. The rest of what determines a positive culture for the staff has to do with the work environment and how staff are treated. Employees are attracted to hospitals with a friendly atmosphere and where management shows it cares about team members. Soliciting staff feedback, showing appreciation, and providing opportunities for employees to learn and grow are all means to developing a positive culture.

RECRUITING AND HIRING STAFF

33

How do I revise my interview questions to make them more effective?

Interviews are the time to screen candidates to determine whether they are good fits for the job and your practice. To get the most out of your interviews, be prepared with a standard set of questions. Interviews are less subjective and it is easier to compare candidates if you ask everyone the same basic questions. In addition, make sure there is a purpose for asking each question. Use job descriptions to identify key areas of performance for each position before beginning the interview process.

Tailor the interview questions relative to the specific job position you need to fill. Don't just ask job candidates general questions about their strengths and weaknesses. Ask more powerful questions, such as "Can you routinely place intravenous catheters in feline and pediatric patients?" or "How would you develop rapport with clients?" Design questions to elicit the information you need to determine whether the potential employee has the right talents, strengths, skills, and knowledge for the job. For every question asked, consider what the answer will tell you about the person's qualifications.

In addition to questions about skill sets, use behavioral questions to ascertain whether a job candidate is likely to act in a way that is consistent with the practice's core values. Use open-ended behavioral questions to assess previous job performance and predict future job performance. For example, the answers to "Tell me about a time when you had to help an angry customer" and "How did you handle the situation?" let you know about an individual's job experience and give you some insight into how they have responded to stressful situations. Another type of behavioral question centers on proposing a specific scenario and asking the candidate how he or she would handle the hypothetical problem.

The following resources can help you in formulating interview questions:

- About.com, www.jobsearch.about.com/od/ interviewquestionsanswers/a/interviewquest2.htm, lists sample interview questions.
- Bnet.com, www.bnet.com/2403-13056_23-52952.html, presents seven interview questions they feel are essential.
- Job Interview Questions, www.jobinterviewquestions.org, teaches how to prepare for effective interviews with job candidates.
- Society for Human Resource Management, www.shrm.org/ TemplatesTools/Samples/InterviewQuestions/Pages/default. aspx, lists sample interview questions by category.

�III➡ **Do It Now**

E-mail mentors or colleagues to ask them whether they would be willing to share their lists of interview questions with you. This can be a good way to find new questions that will work well for your practice.

34

What can I *legally* ask during an interview and when checking references?

For questions to be legal, you should be able to establish that there is a job-related reason for asking them. You must avoid asking any questions that would be discriminatory in nature. Questions that ask about a job candidate's gender, race, age, national origin, religion, sexual preference, disability, arrest record, or financial status are all considered discriminatory.

How questions are phrased also is critical. It isn't unreasonable to want to know whether a potential employee can meet the demands of the job and stay late when necessary. However, asking personal questions such as "Do you have a babysitter?" or "Do you have a car?" is unacceptable. Instead, you need to ask a question such as "Do you have specific times that you cannot work?" Candidates may volunteer personal information you did not specifically ask for. Just be careful not to respond to candidates by engaging in dialogue that is personal in nature and therefore could be considered discriminatory.

Before checking references, obtain permission from the candidate. You should not try to solicit information from reference checks that cannot legally be obtained from the job candidate. The focus of the questions should be on verifying employment information and job qualifications. Typical questions about employment history include checking on employment dates, starting and ending salaries, job title, and whether the employee had a supervisory role. You can also ask why the applicant left the former company, whether the applicant had any warnings or discipline for unexcused attendance, and whether he or she is eligible for rehire. To assess the candidate's job qualifications, you can ask job-related questions such as what the duties and responsibilities of the former job were, what strengths the candidate possesses, how he or she dealt with conflict, and whether the candidate is team oriented.

The Society for Human Resource Management's web site, www.shrm.org/TemplatesTools/Samples/InterviewQuestions/Pages/default.aspx, helps you to pose legal interview questions, and the SHRM publication *Legal, Effective References: How to Give and Get Them* is another excellent resource.

Do It Now

Create a standard form to use when checking references. List the ten to fifteen questions you want to ask to verify employment information and assess job qualifications. Using a form ensures that you stay organized and ask the same questions of all references. This will make your interview process more consistent and effective.

35

How do I hire someone who will end up being the right fit for our practice?

If you want to hire employees who will fit into your culture and be able to excel, you must decide what skills, knowledge, attitudes, talents, strengths, and experience are necessary before you begin the hiring process. You aren't likely to end up with team members you want if you don't define what it means for an employee to be a good fit.

Utilize job descriptions and talk to doctors and staff members to define the requisite skills, knowledge, and experience for each job position. To define the attitudes, talents, and strengths that employees need to be the right fit for your practice, assess critical aspects of your culture so you can hire team members who are in alignment with the practice's core values.

Once you have a clear idea of the parameters for a good job fit, involve multiple team members in the interview process and use working interviews to screen applicants. Working interviews typically involve scheduling the candidate to work a few hours or a full day with your team. This allows the staff to weigh in on whether they think the person may be a good fit for the job. It also gives candidates an opportunity to see firsthand what the job entails and to interact with team members so they can decide whether they will be a good fit for your practice.

Train your doctors and staff to ask specific questions during interviews. Tailor the list of questions to try to obtain information that is relevant for the specific job role and to assess whether the applicant will fulfill job expectations. This helps make the process less subjective and keeps the team focused on assessing job-related qualifications and talents. Coach employees to ask behavioral questions; the answers to these types of questions are a good indicator of whether an applicant will fit in with the practice. Behavioral questions are open-ended questions that help assess the past and future behavior of a candidate. For example, ask potential employees questions about how they like to prioritize tasks, why they are attracted to the position at your hospital, how they have handled conflict with co-workers, and how they would respond to a specific stressful scenario.

ⅠⅡ➡ **Do It Now**

At your next staff meeting, assign team members to work on defining scenarios for behavioral questions. Ask them to think about common situations or problems that occur in the workplace that a new hire will need to be able to handle—for example, responding to an angry client is a scenario faced by client service representatives.

36

How can we attract an associate veterinarian who practices equivalent medicine and models the practice's philosophy when it seems other practices are willing to pay beyond their means just to get someone in the door?

Certainly the practice must offer competitive compensation to attract quality associate veterinarians, but it doesn't make good business sense to pay more than the practice can afford for doctor compensation. In addition to compensation, focus on the benefits of working at your hospital. Get to know something about the candidates you interview so you can identify and highlight positive aspects of the work environment or community that are important to them.

Emphasize specific benefits and strengths of the practice when advertising for associate doctors. Benefits may include high-quality equipment, access to specialists, staff expertise, outstanding patient care, desirable work schedules, CE opportunities, a commitment to client service and education, and low staff turnover. Don't forget to highlight desirable aspects of your community, such as recreational opportunities, outdoor activities, performing arts and cultural events, quality of schools, professional sports teams, affordable housing, vibrant nightlife, variety of restaurants, and other community activities. To augment your advertising efforts, use the practice web site to present more information about the practice and your area. Offer a video tour of the hospital and provide links that may be of interest to out-of-town candidates.

Set up a comprehensive interview process that affords job candidates a chance to get to know your team and culture, the business philosophy, and the level of medicine. If you use working interviews, potential associates can become familiar with staff and see the positive atmosphere of the practice. Emphasize the practice's core values and the attributes of the business that make your practice a desirable place to work. Many job candidates will give up some amount of compensation if they can practice the level of medicine they desire in a rewarding workplace. Also, provide an opportunity to tour the city for candidates who are from out of town.

 ## CHAPTER RESOURCES

Groups and Associations

About.com, www.jobsearch.about.com/od/interviewquestionsanswers/a/
    interviewquest2.htm.

Animal Health Jobs, www.animalhealthjobs.com.

AnimalJobs.com, www.animaljobs.com.

Bnet.com, www.bnet.com/2403-13056_23-52952.html.

CareerBuilder.com, www.careerbuilder.com.

CareerSniff, www.careersniff.com.

CraigsList, www.craigslist.org/about/sites.

DVM360, www.dvm360.com.

iHireVeterinary, www.ihireveterinary.com.

JobConnect.com, www.jobconnectcom.

Job Interview Questions, www.jobinterviewquestions.org.

Monster.com, www.monster.com.

National Association of Veterinary Technicians in America, www.navta.net.

Society for Human Resource Management, www.shrm.org/TemplatesTools/
    Samples/InterviewQuestions/Pages/default.aspx.

Veterinary Career Network, www.veterinarycareernetwork.com.

Veterinary Information Network, www.vin.com.

Veterinary Support Personnel Network, www.vspn.org.

Publication

Bliss, Wendy, JD, *Legal, Effective References: How to Give and Get Them* (Society
    for Human Resource Management, 2002).

37

What is the best training schedule for new hires?

The training schedule for new hires should start with an orientation period of at least one day so that the new employee can begin to learn hospital policies and procedures while becoming comfortable in the new work environment. Provide the new hire with a job description, training schedule, employee handbook, and new-hire paperwork prior to the first day so he or she can review these materials and come prepared with questions. Have the new employee spend the first day with the practice manager and/or a mentor, who will assist with completing any necessary paperwork; give a detailed tour of the hospital; introduce other team members; and provide an overview of the employee manual, job description, safety protocols, and training materials. The orientation period also may include time spent learning the hospital computer system if the new hire is not familiar with the software program.

Training schedules need to be flexible, depending on the experience of the new hire. A minimum of two weeks and up to two months or more may be needed for an employee to understand hospital protocols and procedures as well as learn all the skills for the new job. Assign the new hire to work at least one to two weeks with another experienced team member or mentor in the department to be sure the new employee has mastered the basics. Training schedules need to be detailed and provide a time line for progression. This helps to clarify expectations for everyone.

For training to be successful, be sure to have tools in place to support the training program. This includes a written training manual that outlines the basic skills of the position. Utilize a checklist that contains all the job tasks or job duties a new hire needs to learn. Each line item on the list should have a few columns. In the first column, note when instruction is given; in the next one to three columns, note that the new hire completed the task under the direction of a trainer. The purpose of the columns is to ensure that each job task is checked and dated as it is either taught or performed. Additional training tools may include written handouts, books, videos, DVDs, audiotapes, and online seminars or coursework. Short quizzes at the end of the initial training period help to ensure the employee has understood the material.

Don't forget communication and feedback, as these are critical factors during the training process. If the new hire doesn't feel good about the training, he or she probably will not be happy and won't perform tasks well. Place the new employee with a team member who enjoys training. Be sure to review the new hire regularly in the first ninety days to discuss any problems or concerns.

A useful book that presents training schedules to help you prioritize which new task should be learned first is *Job Descriptions and Training Schedules for the Veterinary Team,* by Wilson and Gendron, available from the AAHA bookstore.

How can I make mentoring effective for staff members other than doctors?

To make mentoring work, you must first establish clear expectations with team members who will be mentors. Discuss the value of mentoring in helping new employees learn and become more proficient. Create a dialogue about how mentors can best assist other team members, and organize a program that outlines their specific job roles. Identify employees who not only have the experience and expertise to mentor but also enjoy teaching. Team members who find teaching and teamwork rewarding will make the best mentors. It can also be helpful to try to pair new hires with experienced employees who match or complement their personality and communication styles.

Next, set up a mentoring program for new hires and any employee who needs to gain skills and knowledge. Start by identifying the most knowledgeable employees to provide guidance to other team members in specific areas, such as laboratory skills, anesthesia monitoring, radiology, pain management, nursing care, client communication, or phone skills, among others. Assign individuals to provide training and answer questions in their areas of expertise. To facilitate adequate training and instruction, arrange to have employees spend some time "shadowing" with a mentor rather than being relied on to do another job.

Mentors need to meet with the staff members they are mentoring on a weekly basis. Use forms and checklists to monitor the employees' progress. Supervisors and managers should also meet regularly with employees involved in mentoring to facilitate feedback and discuss any concerns. Make sure mentors feel valued and not overwhelmed. Check with employees being mentored to ensure they feel they are receiving the instruction and coaching they need to excel.

Where do I find good training materials for my entire staff (receptionist, technician, etc.)?

A number of companies and organizations offer training materials for different members of the veterinary health care team. Regardless of whether you are just starting to develop your training program or need to find additional training materials, start by making a list of training needs for each job position in the hospital. Then research the tools provided by multiple organizations. Check out the list of resources provided at the end of this chapter.

Look for a variety of training tools as you develop your training program. Utilize a combination of videos, DVDs, CDs, webinars, online courses or seminars, lunch 'n' learn seminars by vendors, text-books, articles, quizzes, and written training manuals, depending on the needs of your staff. Animal Care Training (ACT), www.4act.com, offers training videos for purchase and online training with the ability for staff to sign in online, watch videos, and take tests on a variety of veterinary-related subjects; Idexx Laboratories Small Animal Health, www.idexx.com, offers online courses and webinars; Lifelearn, www. lifelearn.com, has a thorough DVD training program with tests; and VetMedTeam, www.vetmedteam.com, offers online courses.

Don't limit yourself to veterinary-related training materials. Training tools for topics such as teamwork, client service, communication, compassion fatigue, conflict resolution, time management, and computer skills can easily be provided by companies outside the veterinary profession.

Some of the best training materials can and should be developed by your own team. Designate a training coordinator to organize the hospital training program and work with team members to create training tools. Training tools developed by the practice can be very effective, especially if they are tailored to the hospital standards and job descriptions. For example, the technical team can help to create a checklist of requisite technical skills with definitions of the necessary proficiency required for two levels of technicians. The checklist can then be used when training new hires. Other tools the team can develop are specific written protocols for job tasks such as placement of catheters, client communication for senior care appointments, and client check-in procedures.

40

How do I get good continuing education for my staff without spending a fortune on flights and hotels?

Many options for continuing education in the veterinary profession don't cost a fortune. Look at a calendar of events for the veterinary profession to see which veterinary meetings are within driving distance, to cut down on the cost of airfare and hotels. One example is the calendar posted at http://veterinarycalendar.dvm360.com/avhc/static/staticHtml.jsp?id=137945. Most states and major cities have seminars and CE programs on a regular basis. Check with the state and local veterinary medical associations to see what programs will be offered for the upcoming year.

Develop a library of CE tools by purchasing textbooks, instruction manuals, CDs, and DVDs for the staff. Subscribe to veterinary publications for the staff to read, and discuss pertinent articles during staff meetings. For example, you can subscribe to *Firstline* magazine and sign up for Firstline seminars, which are offered at the Central Veterinary Conference (CVC) meetings, or contact Veterinary Learning Systems, www.vetlearn.com, which offers *Veterinary Technician* magazine, discussion boards, and articles.

Set up a series of in-house CE seminars that can be given by the doctors and senior staff members. Or take advantage of CE provided by many veterinary companies. A number of pharmaceutical and pet food companies offer hospital lunch 'n' learns and hold local seminars for staff that are informative and practical. In addition, a number of companies now have online courses and webinars for staff members.

You can still send staff to large national meetings, but establish a budget to control costs. Limit the number of employees who attend these meetings each year and/or set a continuing education stipend for each employee. Some employees may decide to pay for their own expenses if the practice pays for the registration.

41

How do I find or make time for complete, consistent, and ongoing training?

You simply must make training a priority. The leadership team has to be committed to a learning environment and willing to make the time for ongoing training. Planning is the key to success. You control your schedule, with the exception of emergencies. For training to be consistent, set a regular schedule and stick with it. Don't forget to take advantage of multiple resources to assist with training, including leveraging the talents of your team members. VetPartners, www.vetpartners.org, can help you find a consultant who can assist your practice with staff training.

Establish an internal continuing education schedule for all of your staff, and announce topics, dates, and times well in advance. Staff training for the entire team can take place once a month at regular staff meetings. Consider closing the practice during this time to ensure there are no interruptions. You also need to establish training sessions for each department so those staff members can learn new skills or knowledge for their specific job roles.

Managers are responsible for overseeing training programs, but they are not typically involved in the actual training. Enlist the assistance of doctors, senior staff members, and team leaders to be responsible for training newer, less experienced employees. Assign at least one trainer to each area of the hospital. Work with these individuals to set up a reasonable training schedule for each department. In-house training programs need to be supported with tools, such as training manuals, books, articles, DVDs, handouts, and web-based resources, to ensure that training is comprehensive and accurate.

Many veterinary suppliers and companies offer training programs such as lunch 'n' learns or online sessions at convenient times for the practice. Take advantage of these free resources and supplement your ongoing training efforts with seminars that employees can attend outside of regular work hours.

�III➡ **Do It Now**

Create a monthly training session for the entire team for the next four to six months. Ask the doctors and staff to submit topics. Then assign a team member to facilitate the training or secure an outside speaker such as an industry representative.

How do I get the staff to understand that the practice is a business and needs to make money?

Open communication between management and staff is very important to help employees understand that the business needs to make money to be successful. Don't talk about the financial health of the practice just in general terms. Give team members actual numbers for hospital expenses and revenues with comparisons with the previous year. Sharing financial data with employees helps them understand the cost of running a business, and they can see that all the income is not profit for the owner. Give staff specific examples of how missed charges, discounts, low productivity, lapses in client service, and wasteful use of supplies negatively affect profitability. In addition, talk to employees about benefits to them, pets, and clients if the practice does well financially. Help them understand that the practice making more money translates into more equipment and drugs, more services provided to clients, and more benefits and compensation to staff.

Get employees involved in attaining practice goals to help them better understand the business side of the practice. Consider assigning employees to specific duties involving overhead expenses so they can better understand hospital costs and are motivated to keep expenses under control. Set goals for the entire team to control expenses and increase production. Then reward success when the staff meets established goals. For example, you could provide a staff bonus to be shared by the entire team at the end of each month if revenue production exceeds that of the year before. You can also set monthly goals for the specific departments, such as the technical team or front office staff. Concentrate goals on a particular service or product, such as scheduling dental cleanings, senior laboratory screenings, or increasing heartworm prevention compliance.

How do I get team members to accept change more easily?

Many employees are apprehensive about change in the workplace and may resist change altogether. Acknowledge to staff that you know change can be difficult. Listen to employees and validate their emotions about how change may affect them or their work environment. Managers who recognize staff concerns and take steps to help employees accept change in a positive way will find that practice transitions occur more smoothly.

Whenever possible, involve the team in decisions that necessitate change. This helps employees understand and buy in to the need for change. It also affords managers an opportunity to identify training needs and solicit ideas from the team to assist with the implementation of changes.

Another way to help staff accept change more easily is to educate them on why change is necessary, discussing how change will benefit them personally or contribute to the success of the practice. For example, if changes will increase efficiency, improve patient care, enhance client service, or increase profitability, then tell this to the employees. Team members are more accepting of change if they see the value to patients and pet owners. They also are receptive to changes that allow for more investment in the practice, such as better equipment, training opportunities, and higher compensation.

Give team members a chance to offer feedback about how they are handling the change once it is implemented. Encourage employees to take on additional responsibilities or assume lead roles in assisting with change. This helps staff take "ownership" of change rather than just feeling like change is being forced upon them.

How do I successfully implement changes in protocols with employees?

People inherently tend to resist change and may be slow to adopt new ways of doing tasks. To be successful, start by including team members in the planning process. Whenever possible, these should be employees who will be responsible for implementing the new protocol or be affected by the change in the planning and discussion phase, even if this involves the entire staff. If employees are given the opportunity to provide input to changes in protocol, they are more likely to accept and support the changes. Staff also often have good ideas about how to implement changes and can give feedback on what training may be necessary.

Next, communicate the forthcoming changes in protocols at a staff meeting so you can explain the reason for the change and address questions prior to implementation. Make sure the team knows the deadline for implementing any change. Follow up by documenting any change to protocols or procedures in the employee manual, and use written communication to remind everyone of the change. You can accomplish this with memos placed in employees' mailboxes, memos posted in central areas, and via e-mail.

When appropriate, use middle managers or team leaders to assist with the training and implementation of any change. For example, if a change is made in a medical protocol, a technician supervisor would be responsible for training the other technicians and answering questions about the new protocols. Finally, be sure to encourage and facilitate feedback from employees to identify whether staff are having any trouble with the change.

45

How do I train and motivate an employee to manage inventory efficiently?

Start by educating the employee who will be responsible for inventory management. This inventory manager needs to understand that inventory control is critical because inventory costs are one of the greatest expenses for the hospital. Share basic financial information with this employee so he or she can see monthly totals for inventory and how an adjustment to this expense affects practice profitability. Be sure to educate the inventory manager on utilizing your computer software so he or she understands how it can help manage the inventory.

After assigning an individual to manage inventory, make sure he or she is trained in all aspects of inventory control. Your inventory manager needs to know reorder points for all inventory items and the importance of inventory turnover ratios to minimize quantities on the shelf. Spend one-on-one time working with the inventory manager to set realistic inventory levels. Provide guidance with respect to ordering large quantities to get a discount. Let the employee know when this may not be a wise expenditure for the practice. Request that your inventory manager seek approval prior to ordering expensive drugs or supplies in bulk.

Meet periodically with your inventory manager to discuss inventory usage, budgets, and any issues related to inventory control. Consider setting monthly or quarterly goals for the employee to minimize inventory costs without running out of inventory. Establish a reward system for attaining the goals. Always give praise for a job well done to show that the employee's efforts are appreciated.

What is the best way to teach the team effective time management?

Start by being a good role model. The team needs to see that you can manage your time wisely and meet deadlines. To teach other team members time management, establish clear job expectations and give staff deadlines to complete job duties. Make sure staff know their daily job responsibilities and set goals for them to accomplish additional work. Then hold employees accountable for meeting job standards and deadlines.

Some employees will be better than others at time management. Mentor and coach those employees who have difficulty knowing how to prioritize their time. You may need to ask the doctors and team leaders to assist with this process. For example, an associate veterinarian or head technician can assist a technician who needs to better understand how to plan when being assigned multiple job tasks.

It is also helpful to solicit feedback from employees about time management. Find out whether lack of training, inefficient work flow, insufficient staff, or lack of proper equipment is hindering their ability to finish job duties on time. Give employees the resources and training they need to excel. Brainstorm solutions to improve efficiency, which will help with time management.

What is the best way to mentor and develop middle managers and team leaders?

Start by defining job duties, job expectations, and desired performance outcomes for middle managers and team leaders. Sometimes supervisors or team leaders are set up to fail because the leadership team hasn't clarified job responsibilities or their level of authority and empowerment. Create written job descriptions and job expectations for all supervisors and identify areas for performance evaluation.

To help middle managers succeed, gradually delegate job duties and make sure the individuals are comfortable with new job duties. When delegating, don't just tell people what to do; instead, show them the best way to accomplish tasks. Share with them your failures as well as your successes in management, and encourage them not to be afraid to fail. Provide ongoing feedback about job performance. Assure managers that you will give them support and guidance so they can be effective in their job roles.

Part of being a good mentor to other employees involves listening to their feedback about job challenges and ideas for enhancing hospital operations. Be open to suggestions from supervisors and flexible if they have a different way of handling job tasks. Middle managers and team leaders may come up with new and improved ways of doing things that you have never considered.

Develop managers by giving them opportunities to learn new skills and advance their knowledge. This includes having them attend leadership meetings and participate in decision making. When decisions are made that involve middle managers or team leaders, encourage problem solving by having them think through alternatives that can be considered and what questions need to be answered to arrive at the best solutions.

CHAPTER RESOURCES

Groups and Associations

Animal Care Training (ACT), www.4act.com.

Exceptional veterinary team, www.myevt.com.

Merial, www.us.merial.com.

Veterinary Hospital Managers Association, www.vhma.org.

Veterinary Information Network, www.vin.com.

Veterinary Learning Systems, www.vetlearn.com. Offers *Veterinary Technician* magazine, discussion boards, and articles.

Veterinary Support Professional Network, www.vspn.org.

VetPartners, www.vetpartners.org. You can find a consultant who can assist your practice with staff training.

Virbac Animal Health, www.virbacuniversity.com.

Publications

Boss, Nan, DVM, *How We Do Things Here: Developing and Teaching Office-Wide Protocols* (AAHA Press, 2009).

Johnson, Spencer, MD, *Who Moved My Cheese?* (G.P. Putnam's Sons, 1998).

Wilson, James F., DVM, JD, and Karen Gendron, DVM, *Job Descriptions and Training Schedules for the Veterinary Team* (Priority Press, 2005).

Wilson, James F., DVM, JD, and Carol McConnell, DVM, *The Veterinary Receptionist's Training Manual* (Priority Press, 1995).

Zachary, Lois J., *Creating a Mentoring Culture: The Organization's Guide* (Jossey-Bass, 2005).

Courses

Firstline, www.dvm360.com. You can subscribe to *Firstline* magazine and sign up for Firstline seminars that are offered at the CVC conferences.

Idexx Laboratories, www.idexx.com. Idexx Laboratories Small Animal Health offers online courses and webinars.

Lifelearn, www.lifelearn.com. This company has a thorough DVD training program with tests.

VetMedTeam, www.vetmedteam.com. Offers online courses.

48

How do I create culture in the face of diversity?

Diversity on the veterinary team may be related to age, gender, nationality, religion, job title, physical appearance, sexual orientation, competency, training, experience, or personality. Diversity within your practice team doesn't preclude developing a positive culture for the practice. In fact, diversity can be very good for the practice as a way to bring a range of ideas and strengths to the team. Rather than being concerned about diversity, focus on the common goal that binds the team together. Make sure everyone knows the practice's mission, goals, and core values. Communicate job expectations to employees and ensure they understand their roles in helping to achieve business success. When the team is working toward a common goal and adhering to the same core values, diversity does not interfere with creating a rewarding culture.

Embrace diversity on the team by asking for feedback from everyone on a regular basis. You may find that employees, as a result of their diversity, present new and different ideas or solutions. Focus on individual talents and strengths of team members that will help the business. For example, a younger team member may be able to offer ideas to enhance the practice web site or start a Facebook page. Another employee may have Microsoft Publishing skills and be able to prepare the hospital newsletter. Other team members may have creative ideas for community involvement, enhancing client education, or improving hospital efficiency. Be sure to leverage the talents of everyone on your team.

What is the best way to break up employee cliques in the practice?

It can be difficult to break up cliques in the practice, so it is advisable to take steps to prevent these groups from forming in the first place. Strive to anchor your team to the mission, vision, and core values of the practice. When everyone is focused on what is best for the hospital, patients, and clients, it is easier to get staff to realize the need to work as a team and to rise above petty differences. It is critical that the practice manager and the doctors model professionalism for the rest of the staff. In your employee policy manual, include standards of conduct that define professional behaviors and outline those behaviors that are unacceptable, such as gossip or demeaning comments about other team members.

If cliques do take hold in the practice, proactively take action to address behavior that is damaging to morale or hospital operations. Talk to staff members about how their behavior is not productive and discuss solutions for any concerns they have about their co-workers. Schedule face-to-face meetings and mediate disputes with employees, if necessary. Emphasize the positive attributes of each employee and remind everyone that teams need to work together toward a common goal.

Sometimes it can be helpful to cross-train employees to work in various departments or to create a rotating schedule so that employees work different shifts with various co-workers. Additionally, you may be able to break up cliques by assigning clique members to special projects or assignments with other staff members so they have the opportunity to see the strengths and talents of those who are not part of their group.

Group activities, such as social activities and team-building activities, are valuable for employees to get to know each other better.

This may foster improved team communication when there is conflict. Ultimately, you may have to eliminate staff who are not team players and who do not support the practice philosophy.

Every few months an employee seems to become the target for blame when things go wrong. How do I avoid this kind of blame game?

Try to prevent employees from blaming others by setting clear job expectations and focusing on teamwork. Remind everyone of their roles in helping the practice reach its vision and goals. When the team stays focused on achieving practice goals, they are less likely to get caught up in blaming co-workers for minor issues. When a mistake occurs, ask the entire team how it could have been avoided and solicit feedback on how to prevent future problems.

If you do notice that someone has become the target of employee complaints, investigate the root of the problem. Make sure the issue is not a question of a misunderstanding regarding policy or procedure. Decide whether the employee involved could benefit from additional training or supervision. Create a plan to provide training, and include team members in the training process.

Determine whether employee blaming involves a personality conflict. Encourage staff members to talk about their differences on their own. If problems continue, schedule a meeting to discuss the issue and mediate the conflict. Brainstorm solutions with the employees and try to achieve buy-in for the steps to a permanent solution.

If an employee is either chronically blamed or chronically blaming others for problems, it may be time to evaluate whether this person is a good fit for the position. Offer training and coaching to modify behavior, but if inappropriate blaming continues, it is time to consider whether the blamed or blaming employee needs to find employment elsewhere. Sometimes an employee is just unhappy, and no amount of action by management will increase his or her job satisfaction.

51

What's the best way to deal with gossip and the rumor mill?

Start by trying to avoid gossip and the rumor mill in the workplace. The best way to minimize gossip is to ensure open communication between management and employees. When open lines of communication exist, gossip and the grapevine are less likely to occur because staff members are informed. People inherently don't like uncertainty or change, so keep the team up-to-date on management actions. Let employees know as soon as decisions are made regarding human resource management, hospital operations, or policies. Even if all you can tell staff is that you haven't yet made a decision, let them know the current status for any changes that may affect their jobs.

Include a no-gossip policy in the hospital employee manual, which will help to establish clear expectations and consequences regarding gossip. Some hospitals also discourage gossip and rumors by addressing this behavior in a standard of conduct or professionalism section in the employee manual.

Once managers realize that gossip is taking place, they should take immediate action to dispel rumors. Meet with the person(s) involved in gossip. Create open dialogue about any rumors or misinformation regarding the practice. If an employee is guilty of gossiping about another employee, take action to mediate disputes, if necessary, and prevent harassment. Let employees know that gossip is damaging to the culture and will not be tolerated. Utilize team leaders and supervisors to discourage gossip and to keep staff informed.

If an employee persists in spreading rumors and gossiping, it is time to decide whether that person is actually a good fit for the practice. As with all inappropriate behaviors, document incidents and terminate problem employees who refuse to change.

52

How do I create and keep a culture of educating and learning for both clients and the team?

Start by ensuring that the practice's mission, vision, and core values reflect a commitment to ongoing education and continual learning. Then communicate with team members regularly about their roles in fulfilling the mission and upholding the core values. Everyone must understand how raising their level of knowledge and enhancing client education can improve patient care and help clients make decisions for their pets. During performance reviews and staff meetings, recognize employees' achievements in learning and educating clients.

Encourage employees to seek continuing education on their own, and provide opportunities for learning. Send staff to seminars and invite industry representatives to the hospital to give presentations. Make sure that employees who attend outside continuing education programs bring back information and ideas to share with the rest of the team. Challenge staff to learn new skills and gain knowledge by assigning projects or setting goals that will further their education and enhance client communication. Leverage the talents and knowledge of doctors and licensed technicians to train and educate other team members during monthly or quarterly continuing education sessions.

To maintain a culture of education and learning, emphasize the importance of continual improvement for employees to gain new skills and knowledge. Strive always to improve with client education as well. Use quizzes and role-playing to test the team's progress in meeting education goals. In addition, recognize employees' accomplishments during performance evaluations.

53

How do I create a culture of accountability in my veterinary team?

Accountability starts with a leadership team that models the behavior they desire from the rest of the staff. Emphasize that everyone on the team needs to uphold the mission, vision, and core values of the practice. Address lapses in accountability by referencing the business's core values. Rather than nagging employees to do something differently, make feedback more powerful by letting them know how their behavior is not consistent with the core values of the practice.

Look for underlying causes for lack of accountability when it occurs. Don't assume an employee has a poor work ethic or bad attitude. Sometimes lack of accountability results because employees don't understand job expectations or they lack training. Clarify job duties and define all areas of accountability for each employee with detailed job descriptions. Then be sure to provide team members with the training they need to excel. For example, if you assign an employee to present treatment plans to clients, make sure that employee has received training on how to talk to clients about money and knows how to interact with emotional clients.

You can also put into place protocols and tools to enhance accountability on a daily basis. For example, you can use checkoff lists that employees must initial once a job assignment is completed. Require that staff initial when medical services are provided or when they make entries in medical records. This allows management to identify who is not accountable and to provide the necessary training or coaching for these employees to improve. To create continued accountability, address unsatisfactory job performance quickly. Talk to staff about errors in a timely manner, while the incidents are still fresh in their minds.

Use staff meetings to discuss team accountability. Create dialogue about any challenges facing the team, and brainstorm solutions to enhance accountability when appropriate. Don't forget to praise staff when a job has been done well. Positive reinforcement for being accountable helps to build a culture of team accountability.

How do we get the owners and leaders of the practice to "walk the talk" consistently?

Make sure the practice has a clear vision and defined core values so that the entire team understands where the business is heading and what behavior is expected. Then constantly evaluate whether everyone, including the owners and leaders, is living the practice's core values and working toward the practice's goals. Strive to open lines of communication so that team members are comfortable reminding both owners and leaders of their roles to walk the talk.

Sometimes owners and leaders don't realize that they aren't being accountable and aren't serving as good role models. Hold regular leadership meetings to review practice goals and discuss roadblocks that are impeding leaders from walking the talk. Managers need to let owners know if their behavior is inconsistent with what is required from the rest of the team. For example, an owner who takes off for a week without notifying the staff until the last minute, even though vacation notice of one month is a staff requirement, can wreak havoc with the schedule and set a poor example. Don't be afraid to let owners or leaders know how their actions affected the staff and the business in such cases. This may be a very difficult conversation to have, but it is essential. It can be helpful to point out to owners how their behavior has negative effects, such as reduced morale and productivity. Consider using outside resources, such as books (see the resource list at the end of this chapter), seminars, and consultants, as a means to improve leadership skills, and discuss how enhanced leadership will drive the success of the practice.

Ⅲ➡ **Do It Now**

If your practice does not already have a written mission or vision statement and core values, talk to the practice owners about the need to engage in strategic planning to develop these critical documents. If your mission or vision and core values are just words on paper, start efforts to bring them to life by discussing them at the next staff meeting.

 CHAPTER RESOURCES

Groups and Associations

DVM360, www.dvm360.com.

Society for Human Resource Management, www.shrm.org.

VetPartners, www.vetpartners.org. You can look here to find a list of consultants to assist with human resource management issues.

Publications

Ackerman, Lowell, DVM, DACVD, MBA, MPA, *Blackwell's Five-Minute Veterinary Practice Management Consult* (Blackwell Publishing, 2007).

Blanchard, Ken, *Managing by Values* (Berrett-Koehler Publishers, 1996).

Gerson, Mark, *Leading Through Conflict* (Harvard Business Press, 2006).

Miller, Brian Cole, *Keeping Employees Accountable for Results* (American Management Association, 2006).

Paterson, Kerry, *Crucial Conversations: Tools for Talking When Stakes Are High* (McGraw-Hill, 2002).

Scott, Susan, *Fierce Conversation: Achieving Success at Work and in Life One Conversation at a Time* (Berkley Trade, 2004).

Smith, Carin A., DVM, *Team Satisfaction Pays* (Smith Veterinary Consulting, 2008).

55

How can I encourage communication among team members in a large practice to ensure continuity of care for each patient and consistent education for each client?

Establishing specific communication protocols helps to ensure continuity of care for patients and consistent client education for pet owners. It is essential to create verbal communication protocols, which will help the team to discuss cases, and to follow written communication protocols, which will facilitate accurate medical records and enhance client education.

One of the most effective protocols for verbal communication is to set up "rounds" for case discussion. Most practices have rounds each morning and whenever there is a shift change for personnel. The primary purpose of rounds is to ensure everyone understands the current medical status of hospitalized patients and what has been communicated to the client. Team members can also review the daily schedule so everyone has the same information about patients to be seen that day and relevant client education. Remember to include front office personnel in rounds or at least to give them an update after rounds.

In addition to rounds, continuity of care and client education should be topics for discussion during regularly scheduled staff meetings. This affords team members an opportunity to discuss any problems with patient care or breakdowns in client communication. This dialogue may result in the team realizing the need to change or update the medical standards of care and/or client education protocols.

Written communication protocols are a must for every practice. Timely, accurate, and complete medical records are indispensable to achieve continuity of care and document client education. All team members must be accountable to keep medical records updated. Other internal communication protocols involve using logs, dry erase boards, or computer software to enter messages for co-workers. Communication protocols for clients include using written communication tools such as client handouts on medical conditions and take-home instructions to enhance client education. The American Animal Hospital Association, www.aahanet.org, offers stickers and forms for a variety of uses, including a Dental Record and Take-Home Instructions form. In addition, AAHA provides pet behavior brochures and pet health brochures on a variety of topics.

How do I improve communication between the technicians and receptionists?

Breakdowns in communication or outright conflict between technicians and receptionists can be a challenge, especially as the practice grows. In large part, this can occur because these two staff groups have different job duties and priorities. To address this problem, strive to open up the lines of communication within the team. The first step to improving communication is to focus everyone on the practice's vision and remind them that their roles are all important in achieving the hospital goals. Discuss with all employees how damaging an "us versus them" mentality can be for the team. To foster open communication, facilitate dialogue between the two groups at your regularly scheduled monthly staff meetings. If you also routinely hold separate meetings for front office personnel and the technical staff, send a representative from each group to the other group's meeting. When communication problems arise, ask each group to brainstorm solutions rather than just complaining.

Try to cross-train your employees whenever possible. Cross-training employees to whatever extent possible can help to improve communication because each team member then has a better understanding of the other person's perspective and the challenges that are unique to each position. Employees who are cross-trained can jump in to help wherever they are needed on a busy day. For example, technicians can answer the phone, help a client, or make an appointment, and receptionists can take a client to the exam room to get things started if the technicians are running behind. As part of your cross-training efforts, be sure to set job expectations so all employees know they need to work together as a team to maximize patient care and client service.

Even if you cannot cross-train everyone, consider having employees "shadow" their co-workers. In this way, the receptionist can see how hectic it can be in the treatment room, which may account for unanswered pages on the intercom. Likewise, technicians who spend time at the front desk can experience the difficulties inherent in interacting with multiple clients during busy times.

�III➡ **Do It Now**

Schedule a get-together such as a dinner or a night of bowling so team members—client service representatives and technicians—can get to know each other better in a fun environment.

57

How can I effectively coach my staff not to come to me, as the practice manager, with every question or problem, but to approach the qualified technicians and front office personnel when appropriate?

Coaching your team members to problem solve and seek the assistance of their supervisors, team leaders, or qualified co-workers is time well spent; otherwise, you will spend your time answering questions and "putting out fires" all day. Your job will be easier if you establish clear policies and standard operating procedures (SOPs) for the hospital. SOPs can be developed for everything from how to take a phone message to resolving conflict between co-workers. SOPs provide a written reference for all staff so they know how to handle various situations and to whom to go for direction for questions and problems that arise on a daily basis in the hospital. Enlist the assistance of senior staff members to serve as mentors to new hires to help with training and to answer questions. Establish clear expectations with mentors and trainers, and give them adequate training tools so they can be effective in their jobs and held accountable in assisting new hires.

When an employee comes to you with a question or problem that should be handled by another supervisor or qualified team member, ask whether he or she has checked with this other individual, and then direct the employee to the appropriate person. Make sure you establish and adhere to a clear organizational chart so employees understand the proper reporting structure in the practice. This means your area leaders must be trained and qualified to answer staff questions correctly. Encourage team members to speak directly to each other and try to resolve issues on their own. If an employee has not been able to successfully communicate with the co-worker involved, meet with the employee and the supervisor to address and resolve the issue. You should also coach your team members to come to you with ideas or solutions to problems rather than just questions or complaints. This will show staff that you value their input and help to empower the team.

58

How do I move a team member into a leadership role and have the rest of the team respect that position?

Before offering to promote an employee into a leadership position, carefully evaluate whether that team member has the necessary skills, including communication skills, to succeed and whether he or she is respected by the team. Good candidates for leadership roles have proven that they excel in their position and have already gained the respect of their co-workers by demonstrating leadership qualities. Before moving someone into a leadership role, confirm that the person wants to move up and is willing to assume the responsibilities that come with the new position. Be sure the employee also understands that this will change his or her relationships with co-workers. Once the decision has been made to promote an employee, inform the team about what duties this person will have and support the employee in the new role.

To help facilitate respect for a team member promoted into a leadership role, present a new organizational chart and clearly define the scope of authority and new duties of this position to the rest of the team. Convey to the staff the reasons for the promotion and highlight the skills and talents of the new leader. Be honest about the fact that transitions can be difficult. Gain the team's support by initiating an open conversation about the change and how it will benefit the staff and the organization.

To support new leaders, help them solve problems as they come up, and assist them in learning and growing in their new positions. Establish weekly meetings initially to assess how they're doing and where they need help. Further, show your support by not allowing staff to come directly to you with questions, but keep directing staff back to their area leaders. Tell new leaders that you understand that mistakes may occur, that you trust them to correct the mistakes, and that you will be there to help when needed.

Changes in leadership can be difficult for staff, but if you discuss goals with employees and ascertain what roles they would like to fulfill in the hospital, this will help foster acceptance for those who take on new roles. If everyone is given the same opportunities to learn new skills and expand their responsibilities, it makes transitions easier.

What are some ongoing team-building activities that continue to keep morale high among team members?

Tailor team-building activities for your employees. Every practice team is different, so you will need to find activities that your staff members find fun and rewarding. Try to find activities that allow employees to learn more about one another, which helps build rapport and trust within the team. Consider planning team-building exercises for staff while at work as well as activities for staff outside of work.

Staff meetings are an excellent time for team-building exercises. Consider using the first ten minutes of the staff meeting to have employees share with the team some bit of information about themselves or something good that has happened to them recently. This is also a good time to share positive client comments with the team. Many hospitals find it works well to plan fun, educational games for team building. For example, some practices play a "Family Feud" or "Jeopardy" type of game. They download music from the TV shows and use props such as a podium with a bell. The questions pertain to hospital policies, protocols, medical benefits, or health care services. Prizes are awarded to the winning team.

Activities outside of work can be very rewarding and help your team bond. Consider getting involved in the community by helping a local pet rescue group, participating in a pet health fair, hosting an open house at the hospital in conjunction with a local blood drive, or forming a team to participate in a local charity sports event. You could also form a team and become active in extracurricular events such as bowling, basketball, volleyball, or softball. Talk to employees and find out what they would like to do.

Ⅲ➡ **Do It Now**

Post a question on an Internet veterinary discussion board asking other managers what team-building activities they have found to be fun and rewarding. Then, at the next staff meeting, you can ask your team which activities they prefer and whether they have additional ideas.

How do I work best with the Millennial Generation?

Let's start with a brief summary about the Millennial Generation, also known as Generation Y. These are people (called Millennials) born between the late 1970s and the late 1990s. This generation is highly techno literate and good at multitasking. They have grown up using cell phones, laptops, and the Internet. Texting and instant access to information are a way of life. Millennials are considered to be confident employees who place a high value on family, enjoying life, and working less. Their work ethic is different from that of previous generations—they desire life balance, they question the reason behind work directives, and they don't automatically respect authority figures. Experts who have studied this generation universally report that Millennials want to be mentored and need consistent feedback. They want to learn and be challenged in the workplace. They also need to know the "why" behind job duties and policies.

To work best with Millennials, recognize and accept that this generation may be different in their approach to work, but they can learn and become some of your best employees. Assign mentors to them and set up regular feedback protocols. Give Millennials constant feedback on their job performance so they understand job expectations and how they are doing. Link their job duties to the practice's mission, vision, and core values. Make sure they understand how their job roles further the success of the practice and benefit them personally. For example, discuss how offering exceptional client service helps clients feel more comfortable, helps attract more clients, and is a skill that will help them be more valuable to the practice—which can ultimately mean more compensation.

Get to know Generation Y staff and take a genuine interest in their personal and professional development. Focus on training and set goals for them to learn new skills, work on projects, and gain proficiency in their job duties. Leverage the talents of Millennials by seeking their input for technology-related projects. Enlist them to assist with the business web site or social media endeavors. Your efforts to develop younger workers will increase their productivity, and it will pay dividends in gaining their trust, respect, and job loyalty.

Ⅲ➡ Do It Now

Get a book on the Millennial Generation so you can learn more about working effectively with Millennials.

CHAPTER RESOURCES

Groups and Associations

Eric Chester and Generation Why, www.generationwhy.com.

Publications

Ackerman, Lowell, DVM, DACVD, MBA, MPA, *Blackwell's Five-Minute Veterinary Practice Management Consult* (Blackwell Publishing, 2007).

American Animal Hospital Association, *AAHA Medical Records* (AAHA Press, various years).

American Animal Hospital Association, Pet Behavior Brochures (AAHA Press, 2010).

American Animal Hospital Association, Pet Health Brochures (AAHA Press, 2007).

Blanchard, Ken, *Empowerment Takes More Than a Minute,* Second Edition (Berrett-Koehler, 2001).

Chester, Eric, *Employing Generation Why?* (Chess Press, 2002).

Chester, Eric, *Getting Them to Give a Damn* (Kaplan Business, 2005).

Deal, Jennifer J. *Retiring the Generation Gap: How Employees Young and Old Can Find Common Ground* (Jossey-Bass, 2006).

Lancaster, Lynee C., and David Stillman, *When Generations Collide* (Harper, 2003).

Smith, Carin, DVM, *Team Satisfaction Pays: Organizational Development for Practice Success* (Smith Veterinary Consulting, 2008).

61

What is the best way to evaluate staff performance and growth?

Evaluation of staff performance and growth is an ongoing task that needs to be supported with a formal review process and consistent feedback. Performance evaluations should be completed for all employees annually at a minimum; however, biannual reviews with shorter quarterly or monthly meetings in between are best to make sure employees are on track. These regular meetings afford staff the opportunity to give and receive feedback and to take steps to improve their job performance.

To effectively complete staff job performance and growth evaluations, you must have the proper human resource management tools in place. This starts with written job descriptions and an employee manual that includes hospital policies so employees know what is expected of them. Another critical tool is a comprehensive training program with such items as checklists for skill sets and written quizzes to test knowledge.

For performance reviews, use evaluation forms that are tailored to the employee's job description and job duties to track and measure job performance. These forms should assess the team member's job knowledge, skill sets, "soft skills" such as communication and teamwork, accountability, and adherence to the practice core values. It can be helpful to utilize self-evaluations and 360-degree reviews to augment performance evaluations. With 360-degree reviews, feedback is obtained from the employee's peers, subordinates, and supervisors. Self-evaluations help identify gaps between the employee's and management's perspective regarding job performance, and 360-degree reviews help to assess employees' soft skills and teamwork.

Goal setting is valuable to facilitate employee growth, and attainment of goals helps to measure job performance and growth progress.

Goals should focus on the employee's personal and professional development as well as the practice's success. For example, setting a goal for a technician to gain proficiency with blood pressure monitoring helps the technician gain new skills, enhances patient care, and drives service utilization and revenue.

62

What is the best way to give employees feedback on their job performance?

Giving feedback to employees helps to improve job performance and accountability. The first step to establishing effective feedback protocols is to remember to give employees feedback on a regular basis so they stay informed on what they are doing well and where they need to improve. For feedback to be effective, it also needs to be specific and timely. Give employees feedback as soon as possible after their observed behavior. Provide specific details about job performance rather than just general comments such as "Thanks for doing a good job," or "We need for you to do a better job." Remember, too, that not everyone has the same definition of what is exceptional, good, or poor job performance; what is on time; or what is clean—so give detailed feedback on *how* you want employees to do their job as well.

Be aware of appropriate times and places to give feedback. Follow the old adage, "Praise in public and criticize in private." If you need to discuss inconsistent job performance or failure to complete job tasks, set up a private meeting with the employee. Try to be sensitive to the timing of feedback if an employee is going through a difficult time. This is not to say that managers should avoid giving feedback, but rather that they should convey empathy if an employee is struggling with personal issues and be prepared to offer support such as employee assistance programs.

Feedback needs always to focus on the behavior of the team member, not on intangibles such as attitude or intention—we cannot measure, quantify, or see an employee's attitude or intention, but we can witness behavior and actions. Rather than telling an employee to have a better attitude or to be nicer to clients, specifically cite which words or actions demonstrate his or her poor attitude or poor job performance. For example, you can tell an employee that his or her body language or use of certain words demonstrates a lack of empathy toward clients. When you focus your feedback on specific behavior and actions, the employee will know what needs to be done differently as well as what has been done well.

�III➡ **Do It Now**

Set reminders for yourself on a weekly calendar or create a spreadsheet with each employee's name so you can keep track of giving feedback to team members on their job performance on a regular basis.

How do I set up reward systems for my employees?

When establishing reward systems for employees, consider what outcomes you are trying to achieve and the amount of money you can budget for rewards. With respect to outcomes, decide whether the goal is to reward staff for revenue growth, decreasing expenses, increasing productivity, attracting new clients, improving patient care, or enhancing client service. You may have multiple goals and a variety of reward systems to try to achieve these goals. Rewards are not always monetary, but if you do implement monetary rewards, you need to account for these expenses when budgeting. Reward systems that allocate staff bonuses based on increasing revenues or cutting costs essentially pay for themselves. However, these bonuses do affect net income.

When setting up rewards, clearly communicate the details of the incentive or bonus system to staff. Educate team members on the desired outcome and tell them how their efforts will help the business. For example, you could decide to focus on a particular product or service each month and set a goal of exceeding revenues by 10 percent over the previous year. Define the time period for rewards. For example, a profit-sharing plan may involve bonuses given at year's end, whereas other programs may involve rewards that are given at the end of each month and change each quarter. Keep team members apprised of their weekly or monthly progress so they know how they are doing.

Determine what motivates your staff rather than arbitrarily selecting rewards. Reward systems tailored to individual employee preferences are more likely to encourage employees to achieve specific goals. For example, when gas prices are high, rewarding staff with gas cards is greatly appreciated. Rewards can be in the form of gift cards, staff parties or activities, days off, or cash bonuses.

Remember that reward systems do not always have to include actual "rewards." All team members need to be recognized and acknowledged on a regular basis for excellent job performance. Savvy managers use some type of reminder system to make sure that they are consistently praising employees when they excel. Many practices also set up a reward system for team members to recognize each other's performance. Employees' efforts are typically acknowledged at staff meetings.

How do I begin offering pay incentives and levels of job descriptions (e.g., level I, II, III, IV technicians; client service representatives; and so forth)?

Creating job descriptions with different levels of proficiency and corresponding pay scales for these positions is a two-step process. First, you must establish a foundation for job levels, which starts with developing detailed new job descriptions and establishing criteria for pay incentives or pay scales for each position. Second, you need to implement the new job levels and pay incentives by educating the team about the new system and working with individual employees on developmental plans if they want to attain a higher job level and pay scale.

To create different job levels and job descriptions, begin by assessing the skill sets, proficiencies, and job duties performed by your current employees. This will help you decide how many levels in each job role make sense for your practice. Involve your staff in this process by asking them to list their job tasks or duties and what skill levels they want to learn. Don't forget to ask for feedback from doctors as well. You will need to clearly establish what skills and levels of proficiency are required to be promoted to the next job level. Then, assign pay scales according to the experience, qualifications, and skill levels that are needed for each job level. To gain a higher job level and associated compensation, employees will need to demonstrate improved skills and qualifications.

Once you have developed job descriptions and pay differentials for each level, meet with the team to explain the new concept as a whole and to answer questions. Then meet individually with each employee to review his or her current job level and pay scale. To afford staff the opportunity to move to a higher job level, you must have a training program in place. Tailor training tools to the job levels, and outline how employees can learn new skills or duties. Establish realistic time frames for employees to gain higher job levels and assign specific mentors or trainers to oversee training for each job level.

How do I handle an employee who constantly complains?

Always investigate the validity of staff complaints. Even when an employee who complains constantly comes to you with a concern, determine whether his or her complaint is about an issue that legitimately needs to be addressed by management. For example, if the employee complains about the work load, check whether others are completing their job assignments. If one employee complains about another employee, see whether the concern is valid.

Talk to employees who habitually complain and seek to understand why they are unhappy. Ask them whether anything is bothering them. Do they want to talk about issues in the clinic? Are they bored? Do they need to be challenged? Ask them what you can do to make their jobs easier. These employees may not realize how much they are complaining. Employees appreciate the opportunity to be heard, and you may be able to redirect the employees' need to feel involved into a particular project within the practice. Let employees who constantly complain know that their behavior negatively affects morale, teamwork, and client service and is disruptive to the practice. Make sure they understand that their cycle of negativity must stop.

Another way to handle employees who complain is to move them to positive action. Tell staff that they must offer possible solutions when they come to you with problems. At first you will likely need to coach team members to become problem solvers. If they don't present solutions, you may need to ask them how they think the problem should be resolved. For example, you could suggest that they create a training checklist or instructional handout for the team if they complain about job tasks not being completed properly. When you teach employees to solve problems themselves rather than solving issues for them every time, you can develop employees with greater job satisfaction who are more productive.

Let employees who continue to be unhappy and constantly complain about issues that aren't bothering other people or issues that cannot be fixed know that they may need to consider whether their position is a good fit for them. Sometimes termination is the only solution to deal with employees who negatively affect the business culture.

An excellent resource regarding complaining employees is *The No Complaining Rule: Positive Ways to Deal with Negativity at Work* by Jon Gordon (Wiley, 2008).

What is the best way to handle disciplinary problems?

Managers need to establish and adhere to disciplinary policies that are consistent and fair. Employees should know what actions justify disciplinary procedures and what the consequences are for unacceptable behavior. The employee handbook can be used to outline your disciplinary policy and the behaviors that are grounds for termination. Don't procrastinate when handling disciplinary problems, or accountability will suffer and you will risk losing the respect of the other employees. When it is necessary to take disciplinary action, meet privately with the employee involved and document the conversation.

When meeting with an employee, start by giving specific examples of unacceptable behaviors or poor job performance. Then ask the employee about the problem in question to ascertain the reasons for the behavior and to give the employee an opportunity to explain his or her side of the story or any extenuating circumstances. This will help uncover whether there is an underlying problem, such as lack of training. Clearly articulate what behavior is expected from the employee and what actions need to be taken to resolve the issue, and set a date to meet again. Be clear about the consequences of noncompliance with hospital policies.

When handling disciplinary problems that are more serious or are a result of failure to follow through with action to resolve previously discussed problems, you need to take steps outlined in the formal disciplinary policy. This generally includes progressive disciplinary actions (a verbal warning, written warning, suspension, and termination) so each related incident of unacceptable behavior by the employee triggers a more severe response to encourage the employee to modify the behavior. Document disciplinary actions, and if a warning is given, use a form to indicate the type of warning, the specifics (e.g., dates of unexcused absences), the expectation from the employee going forward, and the time frame for this expectation. Both manager and employee need to sign warning forms. If an employee refuses to sign, note this on the form and have a witness sign that the employee received a copy of the notice. Depending on the nature of the disciplinary problem, you may elect to give the employee multiple warnings prior to the final warning and termination. Just be sure to follow through with consequences for noncompliance once a final warning is issued.

What consequences can I use for policy infractions such as unexcused absences and tardiness?

Ultimately, problems with employee behavior such as unexcused absences and tardiness justify following a progressive disciplinary policy. But first try to avoid the need for disciplinary action. This starts with making sure you have a well-defined attendance policy in the hospital policy manual. Clearly establish job expectations so employees understand that being on time and being dependable are conditions of employment and part of the practice culture.

Track employee absences and tardiness, and immediately address policy infractions. Meet with the employee to discuss the problem and determine whether the employee needs some type of assistance. You may be willing to change the employee's schedule if he or she is a valued team member who now needs different hours. Direct the employee to outside assistance for personal problems. Let the employee know how the behavior impacts the practice, and reinforce job expectations for the future. Be sure to document the meeting in the employee's file.

If unexcused absences or tardiness continues, follow your hospital's disciplinary policy. Typically, practices use progressive discipline, which includes a verbal warning, one or more written warnings, possible suspension, and termination. Although no one likes to terminate an employee, attendance problems must be addressed by management. Otherwise, accountability and morale suffer as the team realizes that there are no consequences for some unacceptable behaviors.

Don't forget that it is also important to recognize and reward employees for good attendance. You can reward perfect attendance with a bonus day off or a monetary award. Some practices institute a point system for attendance and reward employees if they receive a certain number of points.

How do I decide whether, or when, to terminate an employee who is liked by the team, demonstrates definite areas of skill, but then completely underperforms in other respects?

For an underperforming employee, first complete a thorough evaluation of the employee's strengths, job performance, and dedication toward improving. Consider how significant the area of weakness or lack of skills is for the success of the practice. For example, assess whether the areas of inadequate job performance jeopardize patient care, affect client service, or interfere with teamwork. Determine whether lack of training is a problem, or whether the employee lacks the talent to perform well in the area of weakness. Identify whether it might be possible to reassign the employee to a different area of the hospital where he or she can excel.

Before deciding on termination, afford the employee every opportunity to improve by establishing job expectations, providing training, and offering feedback on job performance. Outline specific action steps with deadlines for the employee to meet job standards. Use employee evaluations at appropriate intervals to let the employee know how he or she is progressing.

If job performance does not improve despite training and feedback, follow a progressive disciplinary policy up to and including termination. When making a decision on whether to terminate an employee, remember to focus on what's best for the business rather than on how well-liked the employee is by the rest of the team. Being popular does not make an employee an asset to the company. Even if team members like an employee as a friend, they are still aware of this person's performance problems. Mature employees understand valid decisions to terminate a co-worker.

CHAPTER RESOURCES

Groups and Associations

DVM360, www.dvm360.com.

Society for Human Resource Management (SHRM), www.shrm.org.

VetPartners, www.vetpartners.org. You can look here to find a list of consultants to assist with human resource management issues.

Publications

Ackerman, Lowell, DVM, DACVD, MBA, MPA, *Blackwell's Five-Minute Veterinary Practice Management Consult* (Blackwell Publishing, 2007).

American Animal Hospital Association, *AAHA Guide to Creating an Employee Handbook*, Third Edition (AAHA Press, 2009).

Blanchard, Ken, and Spencer Johnson, *The One Minute Manager* (Berkley Trade, 1986).

Blanchard, Ken, and Robert Lorber, *Putting the One Minute Manager to Work* (HarperCollins Business, 2000).

Blanchard, Ken, William Oncken, and Hal Burrows, *The One Minute Manager Meets the Monkey* (William Morrow, 1991).

Blanchard, Ken, Eunice Parisi-Carew, and Donald Carew, *The One Minute Manager Builds High Performing Teams* (William Morrow, 1991).

Collins, Jim, *Good to Great* (Harper Business, 2001).

Fleming, John H., and Jim Asplund, *Human Sigma* (Gallup Press, 2007).

Gendron, Karen, DVM, *Practical Guide to Performance Appraisals* (AAHA Press, 2002).

Gordon, Jon, *The No Complaining Rule: Positive Ways to Deal with Negativity at Work* (Wiley, 2008).

Smith, Carin A., DVM, *Team Satisfaction Pays* (Smith Veterinary Consulting, 2008).

Wilson, James F., DVM, JD, and Karen Gendron, DVM, *Job Descriptions and Training Schedules for the Veterinary Team* (Priority Press, 2005).

How do I retain good employees?

The first step to retaining good employees is to provide competitive compensation and benefits. Employees may not be drawn to veterinary jobs for the money, but they will leave if you don't have an attractive pay and benefits package. In addition to compensation, you can effectively retain staff if you maintain a positive work environment and focus on employee development.

Create a work environment that makes people want to come to work by building a positive culture. One of the best ways to do this is to make sure team members feel valued. Routinely let staff know you appreciate their efforts and care about their well-being. Maintain an open-door policy so employees can communicate with management when they have concerns or ideas to share. If you listen to staff feedback, employees know they are valued and part of the team. In addition, keep team members informed about hospital decisions and quickly address any conflict that may arise between co-workers. This helps to build trust and respect between management and staff.

Employee development is a good way to retain good employees who want to be challenged and learn new skills. Giving team members new responsibilities and providing ongoing training allow them an opportunity to grow personally and professionally. Use staff meetings to provide education for the entire team, but implement tailored developmental plans for each employee as well. Developmental plans should identify individual training needs and outline monthly or quarterly goals for employees to learn new skills or knowledge. When employees attain a higher level of skills, knowledge, and experience, you can reward them with increases in pay. This further assists with efforts to increase retention.

ⅠⅢ➡ **Do It Now**

Conduct a staff survey to find out more about the level of job satisfaction for your employees. You can find a sample employee survey on the Society for Human Resource Management's web site, www.shrm.org, or at www. SurveyMonkey.com.

70

How can I hire and keep good kennel assistants?

Practices often experience higher turnover of employees who work in the kennel department because of the nature of the job duties and lower wages. One of the ways to hire and retain good kennel assistants is to enhance your recruitment process for this position. Many hospitals find it helpful to focus recruitment efforts on students who are interested in pursuing a career in veterinary medicine. These job candidates are more likely to take pride in their work and have a desire to learn. In addition, consider advertising for "animal caretakers" rather than "kennel help" to attract more qualified applicants whom you will be able to train and develop. Emphasize that you are looking for employees who will act professionally and adhere to high standards of quality care for pets.

Another way to improve retention is to develop a thorough interview process to identify candidates who will be the right fit for the job. Establish a structured interview involving multiple team members to ask specific questions so you can better assess whether applicants have the right attitude and ability to learn. Set up working interviews for top candidates to give them an opportunity to fully understand the job duties. This allows your team to observe the prospective team members actually working—how they interact with the rest of the team, how they relate to animals, and whether they can follow directions.

Once you hire employees to work in the kennels, increase the likelihood that they will stay by focusing on their development. Cross-train kennel workers to assist the technical team and client service representatives. This allows them to learn new skills and adds variety to their job duties. Provide ongoing continuing education to kennel assistants to keep them challenged and enhance their knowledge.

Don't forget to let kennel employees know they are valued team members. Include them in staff meetings and seek their input on hospital operations and proposed changes. When kennel staff feel appreciated and part of a team, they tend to work harder and stay longer.

71

How do I keep my staff consistently motivated to do their jobs properly?

One of the best ways to motivate staff is to give them regular feedback. Give consistent feedback on job performance and solicit feedback from employees by asking, "How are you doing?" and "How can I help you in your job?" Team members value two-way feedback because it validates their hard work, lets them know how they can improve, and affords them an opportunity to offer input on how to enhance hospital operations.

Another critical aspect of staff motivation that is often overlooked is the importance of training. Sometimes poor job performance occurs because of boredom or a lack of proficiency as a result of insufficient training. Comprehensive training programs enhance employee motivation by affording staff the opportunity to learn new skills and knowledge so they can excel in their jobs. Most employees welcome the chance to take advantage of training and continuing education programs.

Never underestimate the motivational power of praise and recognition. All employees like to know that management cares about them and appreciates their contributions to the practice's success. However, not everyone is motivated by the same recognition. Get to know team members to better understand what type of recognition will enhance motivation. Some employees like public recognition at staff meetings, whereas others are more appreciative of a handwritten thank-you note.

Some practices routinely use monetary rewards to motivate employees to achieve goals. Bear in mind that monetary rewards such as bonuses, gift cards, pet health credits, and time off may motivate staff to achieve goals, but the results tend to be temporary. Change the goals and the rewards on a regular basis to keep employees motivated consistently. For rewards to motivate job performance, they must also be tailored to the employees. Some employees may be motivated by more responsibility and extra projects, whereas others may be motivated by time off, gift cards, or a gift basket.

72

How do I keep employees motivated even during difficult financial times?

During difficult financial times, it is easy for negativity to bring down employee morale and productivity. To keep employees motivated, maintain an upbeat, positive attitude and open lines of communication between management and staff. You can eliminate uncertainty and the associated stress by keeping employees updated on the financial status of the practice. Give employees feedback on plans to keep the business on track financially. Let employees know the reasoning behind any management changes that affect operations or compensation.

Focus on how everyone needs to work together to achieve the practice goals. Try to set goals for staff that will help increase revenues and profitability. Encourage team members to contribute ideas for growing the practice, improving productivity, and controlling expenses. You may even be able to give small gifts to employees with the best ideas and put them in charge of implementing their suggestions. Setting goals can help staff be more willing to try harder to schedule clients for appointment, explain the benefits of services, adhere to practice standards, and work more efficiently.

Try to have fun at work so the work environment doesn't become too negative. No one wants to work at a practice where they are not happy. Recognize successes each week and at staff meetings. Be creative with ways to enhance the workplace atmosphere. For example, you can use music, post funny or positive quotations, play trivia contests, hold potluck lunches, or celebrate birthdays.

Arrange to have industry representatives give seminars and provide lunch to the staff. This helps keep the team trained and motivated to better communicate with clients about products and services, which in turn helps drive the financial success of the practice.

73

What are some suggestions for fun pick-me-ups for the employees that don't cost a lot of money?

Efforts to create fun in the workplace and show staff appreciation help build a positive culture where people want to come to work. There is no limit to suggestions for ways to have some fun and lift team spirit. Solicit ideas from employees if you have difficulty coming up with creative ideas. It also helps to vary activities or rewards so you have the ability to surprise team members. Otherwise, some rewards become expectations rather than fun pick-me-ups.

Food seems to be universally appreciated by staff. Keep candy in a bowl on your desk or in the break room. Periodically provide additional treats for staff, such as ice cream bars or other snacks. Celebrate birthdays with the type of cake or snacks requested by the person having the birthday. Have refreshments at staff meetings. Take advantage of lunch 'n' learns by vendors. Each month, allow a different team member to pick where you will order lunch.

You can also organize fun activities, some of which may occur outside of regular work hours. The following activities are enjoyable and don't cost much money: local walks for various charities; staff picnics; bowling nights; sledding; Easter egg hunts; scavenger hunts; Spirit Fridays with small prizes for "Best in Show" (decide on a theme for Spirit Friday—it could be that everyone wears funny or silly ties or scarves or dresses up according to an upcoming holiday); vote on joke of the week (must be appropriate for the workplace); and a Halloween costume contest for clients, pets, and employees.

Other fun pick-me-ups for staff that aren't expensive are free movie rental vouchers, movie tickets, gas cards, gift cards, and paid hours or a full day off. Many practices use some sort of fake money rewards ("Bonus Bucks" or "Kudos Bucks") that are handed out when employees give exceptional service, demonstrate superior job performance, or go out of their way to help co-workers. Once a team member collects a certain number of fake dollars, he or she can redeem them for a gift or reward.

74

How do I motivate a good team into a great team?

Start by anchoring the team members to the practice's vision and making them a part of achieving this vision. Strive to develop a culture in which employees feel like they have some "ownership" in the business. Create an atmosphere in which employees feel they are empowered to give input and play a role in the success of the practice. Include team members in as many discussions about policy, operations, and planning as possible. By allowing a good team the opportunity to play an integral role in accomplishing practice goals, you can inspire them to be a great team that reaches higher levels of job performance.

It takes time to turn a good team into a great team. For the practice team to be great, focus on employee development and empowerment. Recognize, develop, and leverage the strengths of individuals that will benefit the team as a whole. Work with employees to set goals for them to learn new skills, gain knowledge or proficiency, and work on hospital projects. Then empower team members to achieve their goals and those of the practice. To empower employees, coach them to problem solve and take action that is consistent with the vision and core values of the practice. Give them new tasks or challenges and provide feedback on their job performance. Employees need boundaries, but they also need to know that they are allowed to make mistakes. If mistakes are made, let staff know how they could have acted differently, and they will learn from their mistakes.

Encourage employees to work together to achieve goals and celebrate success within the team. Praise employees for their efforts and reward exemplary job performance. Teams that perform at a higher level and contribute to the success of the practice deserve to reap benefits. Praise certainly is invaluable, but increased compensation and monetary rewards can help to motivate greater job performance.

CHAPTER RESOURCES

Groups and Associations

DVM360, www.dvm360.com.

Society for Human Resource Management (SHRM), www.shrm.org. SHRM is a comprehensive resource for human resource management that offers articles, publications, conferences, tools, and forms on a variety of topics.

SurveyMonkey, www.surveymonkey.com.

VetPartners, www.vetpartners.org. VetPartners is a national association whose membership includes experienced veterinary consultants. You can visit their web site to find a consultant to help you with human resource management.

Publication

Ackerman, Lowell, DVM, DACVD, MBA, MPA, *Blackwell's Five-Minute Veterinary Practice Management Consult* (Blackwell Publishing, 2007).

Courses

Veterinary Management Institute (VMI), www.aahanet.org/education/vmi.aspx. VMI is a comprehensive "mini-MBA" program for veterinary professionals offered by AAHA and Purdue University. One of the four management modules is on human resource management.

75

What is the most effective way to answer the phone within three rings in a busy veterinary practice without using an automated phone service?

Most clients don't like an automated phone service, so it is best to use this option only to assist callers who are looking for basic information only, such as hours of business, address, or a fax number. To answer the phone in an effective manner, start by making sure that every team member answers the phone with a standard greeting that states the practice name and the employee's name (e.g., "ABC Veterinary Hospital, this is Karen"). After this greeting, staff can ask, "How may I help you?" or "How may I direct your call?" Remind employees that this greeting needs to be clear so the caller can understand them. Team members must also always answer the phone with a smile and friendly tone of voice to engage clients and put them at ease.

To ensure the phone is answered within three rings, cross-train the entire hospital team to be responsible for phone calls. If the phone rings more than three times because a receptionist is busy, technicians or kennel assistants may answer the call and ask the callers to please wait, if necessary, while they get someone who may assist them.

The front desk must be appropriately staffed so that each call can be answered in a timely fashion and hold times can be kept to a minimum. Ideally, phones should be answered in a separate area, away from where clients are checked in and out. This improves efficiency and avoids distractions for clients at the front desk and for employees answering phone calls. If this is not possible, consider dedicating one or more client service representatives to answer the phones at all times, and rotate this role if warranted. When clients must be placed on hold, have the staff member always inquire first whether the client has an emergency and ask for permission to place the caller on hold. If a hold time will be excessive, have the staff member ask the caller whether a call-back would be okay, and then be sure this is done within the promised time frame.

ⅲ➡ **Do It Now**

Create a written standard for answering the phone. The standard should include specifics such as what greeting employees are to use, answering the phone by the third ring, not leaving callers on hold for longer than one minute, and asking permission before placing callers on hold. Distribute the standard to team members at the next staff meeting and discuss any questions they may have.

76

What is the best way to reach clients for call-backs during the day when they might be at work or elsewhere?

The best way to reach people to give them information about their hospitalized pets during the day is to be proactive in obtaining several contact numbers from the clients upon admission and letting them know approximately when you will be calling. Ask clients, "When is the best time of day to reach you?" Note this information on new client forms or in the medical record. Alternatively, you can ask clients to call at designated times, which may reduce the chances that you will miss them when you call. You can also use e-mail or text messages to communicate with clients if your communication is not urgent. When leaving messages, it is important to leave your name along with the phone number so the client knows whom to ask for when returning your call.

When doing call-backs to check on the status of a pet that has been discharged or calls to remind clients of their appointments, you can try to call people at the end of the day, when they are more likely to be at home. It is also helpful when pets are discharged from the hospital to ask clients which number to call and what time of day is best to call to check on the pet. It is a good practice to call several times when checking on pets before assuming the pet is fine.

77

How do I achieve excellent customer service at my front desk?

Achieving excellent client service at the reception desk starts by hiring the right staff. Recruit and hire employees who enjoy interacting with people and helping clients—even when it is stressful. Look for client service representatives (CSRs) who have the talents and attitude you need to provide outstanding client service. The leadership team also needs to create a culture that is client centered if you want to attain high levels of service. This starts with making sure that achieving the highest level of customer service is part of your mission and a core value of the practice.

To ensure that your team consistently delivers exceptional service, you need to provide customer service training for both new hires and current employees. Training needs to encompass all aspects of client service, including effective communication skills, phone skills, operational efficiency, and rapport with clients. You can also create service standards and then train the team to adhere to these standards. This ensures that CSRs provide excellent service and can be a means to raise the level of service in your practice. Several books listed in the resources at the end of this chapter address client services.

Achieving excellent client service is an ongoing process. To be successful, you need to commit to continuous improvement, always looking for ways to enhance service. Establish weekly or biweekly client service meetings to discuss complaints, challenges, progress, and ideas and opportunities to exceed client expectations. For example, you can periodically role-play such client interactions as how to effectively respond to an angry client.

Measure the current level of service by using client surveys or a "mystery shopper." A mystery shopper is someone you can hire to call or visit your practice and provide a report on the level of client service. This can be a practice management consultant or someone in a company that provides this service. Carin A. Smith's book, *Client Satisfaction Pays* (AAHA Press, 2009), discusses the mystery shopper concept in detail. Use the information you obtain to set goals to improve service ratings or address weaknesses in service.

78

How can we attract new clients?

To attract new clients, use a variety of marketing efforts aimed at increasing awareness and promoting the practice's services to area pet owners. To do this, you will need to engage in some forms of advertising. Advertising can take many forms with different levels of cost and success. Find what works best for your practice by measuring the results of your efforts and continue the initiatives that work best. New practices often need to do more advertising than established practices, but even long-standing practices may need to engage in some form of targeted advertising to increase the number of new clients coming in.

Traditional advertising includes hospital signage, yellow page ads, the Internet, and local newspaper ads. Other options are targeted mailings, radio announcements, and press releases. Don't forget that one of the best forms of advertising is the practice's web site. Check with your maintenance provider about ways to enhance your site's web presence. Make sure you have comprehensive information on the web site for new clients to learn about your practice.

To further increase awareness of your hospital, have staff maintain a presence in the community by participating in local activities such as festivals, parades, school career days, pet adoptions, fundraisers for humane societies or shelters, sporting events, and area business organizations (e.g., the Chamber of Commerce). Give your staff logo-wear and business cards, and encourage them to promote the practice when they are away from work. Look for opportunities to attract clients by giving client education seminars, holding periodic open houses, and offering free exams to pets adopted from a shelter or purchased at local pet stores.

In addition to advertising or creating a presence in the community, the most powerful way to reinforce your marketing efforts is through word-of-mouth recommendations from your existing clients who are pleased with your services. Practices that strive to provide exceptional quality care for patients and service to clients can grow their business through client referrals. Make sure the hospital is a warm and welcoming place that clients want to recommend to their friends. Send thank-you notes to clients who make referrals. You can also reward existing clients with a client loyalty program that offers a hospital credit, discounted service, or a free service for each new client who is referred.

79

How do I stop the outflow of clients to neighboring practices who undercut our prices?

Train your team to explain to phone shoppers and existing clients the difference between your services and lower-cost alternatives. Thoroughly explain details about services and procedures to clients, focusing on the benefits for the pet and the client. Explain the need for individual services and why your services may cost more. Make sure the clients are comparing apples with apples and that they understand the old adage "You get what you pay for." Encourage phone shoppers to visit the practice and offer to give them a tour so they can see for themselves the quality of medical care your hospital can provide.

It is critical that your staff understand the need for and value of the services offered so they can educate clients. Use staff meetings to discuss the importance of perceived value and specific benefits of your services. Engage the team in a brainstorming session about what differentiates your services and what value you create for clients. Examples are longer appointment times, laser surgery, extended business hours, availability of specialists, additional services not offered elsewhere (e.g., complementary medicine or puppy socialization classes), advanced diagnostics, or an interactive web site with valuable client education articles and links. This brainstorming session will help your team to understand and communicate to clients all the values your practice offers. Once team members realize that clients can't appreciate what they don't know, they are more aware of the need for communication that clearly conveys what differentiates your services from those of other practices.

You must also provide value to clients so they remain loyal to your practice. Cost is not as likely to be an issue when the perception of value is high. Rather than trying to compete on price with neighboring practices, focus on providing excellent patient care and fantastic client service. Team members must continuously strive to differentiate your service by exceeding client expectations. Once clients realize the great value they receive from your practice, they won't be tempted by low prices to go elsewhere. Building relationships with clients and communicating that you care about them and their pets will make clients reluctant to leave your practice.

Do It Now

Develop a one-page handout for staff that highlights the questions they should ask to engage price shoppers. Create a second document that lists routine services and associated benefits so team members can use this as an easy reference when talking to callers about what is included with the cost of routine procedures such as an ovariohysterectomy. Employees can then offer to mail this information, along with a hospital brochure, to all price shoppers.

Do It Now

Set a goal for the staff to help increase the number of new clients each month. Start an incentive program for staff to reach their goal so they are even more motivated to give potential new clients the information they need to help them make an appointment. The incentive might be gift cards for team members who bring in new clients who were phone shoppers.

What are the most effective marketing techniques for companion animal practices?

The first key to effective marketing is to focus on both internal and external marketing initiatives. Internal marketing includes efforts to increase utilization of services by existing clients. Internal marketing also involves efforts by the practice to train and motivate staff to work together as a team to better meet client needs. External marketing is written or verbal communication aimed at increasing awareness and attracting new clients. Decisions regarding how many resources to allocate to internal versus external marketing are tailored to the business's goals and based on assessments of which types of marketing will yield the greatest benefits for the practice. The second key to implementing effective marketing efforts is to track the success of specific tactics to better determine which efforts to continue and when to execute different or additional marketing initiatives.

Some of the most effective external marketing techniques are highly visible hospital signage, advertisements, client mailings, hospital web sites, and community involvement. The desired amount of advertising and type of advertising vary considerably. Most practices now utilize online sites for advertising as much as or more than print phone book ads. To better determine how much money to spend for advertising and which ads are most useful, calculate the return on investment for these expenditures—assess how many new clients come to the practice as a direct result of your advertisements. Community involvement can be a particularly effective marketing technique because it allows members of the practice to educate potential clients about the hospital's services. For example, you can speak about pet health care and your hospital at Rotary or Chamber of Commerce meetings, or you can give presentations to breeder groups.

Many practices find that internal marketing is the best use of time and money. Taking care of your existing clients by providing high-quality, comprehensive health care to pets and exceptional service will increase service utilization and bring in referrals. Don't forget to train the staff to explain the benefits of veterinary services, which helps drive compliance. To further increase service utilization, look at your current client base and send out reminder postcards, e-mails, mailings, or newsletters to certain groups of your clients on specific preventive health care topics or medical conditions. For example, you can promote senior exams and laboratory testing to all clients with pets over age seven. You can also increase service utilization by looking at which services are underutilized. Look at computer reports to see how you are doing with recommendations and compliance for services such as dental cleanings, feline wellness examinations, laboratory testing, and heartworm tests. Look for areas of opportunity by assessing data for the number of patients who had services performed, such as urinalysis, blood pressure checks, radiographs, and ultrasound. Consider whether you need to do a better job recommending these services and educating clients about the value of these services.

81

How can we improve client retention?

To improve client retention, you must build strong relationships with clients. When clients form bonds with the veterinary team, they will keep coming back. To bond clients to the practice, take the time to develop rapport with them, gain their trust, and demonstrate that you genuinely care about them and their pets. Let pet owners know that you are patient advocates by providing high-quality medical care and educating clients about preventive health care. Listen to clients and make them partners in decisions regarding their pets. An excellent resource for this is *Educating Your Clients from A to Z* by Nan Boss (AAHA Press, 1999).

Although clients visit veterinary hospitals for medical care for pets, it is often the level of client service and perception of value of services that determine whether they remain loyal clients. Remember that every contact with a client—whether on the phone or in person—has an effect on the service experience. Make sure the reception area and exam rooms are warm, inviting, and comfortable. Train employees on how to connect with clients and deliver sophisticated, professional service. Much of staff training needs to focus on developing excellent communication skills and making sure employees are knowledgeable so they can educate clients about the benefits of services for their pets. Give clients comprehensive health care information by augmenting verbal communications with monthly newsletters, information packets, and postings on the practice web site.

To further enhance value for pet owners, strive to exceed their expectations. Have the team brainstorm ways to "wow" clients with your service. Solicit feedback from clients on how you can improve your service. Periodically survey clients to see how you are doing and always respond to clients who are dissatisfied. Look for opportunities to thank clients. Be sure to acknowledge and reward client referrals. When clients feel appreciated and know how much you care, client retention will improve.

⫸ **Do It Now**

Create a short (ten questions or less) client satisfaction survey. The survey can be mailed to clients, handed out after appointments, or posted on the practice web site. Check www.SurveyMonkey.com for assistance in developing an online survey. Be sure to assess the survey results on a regular basis.

82

How do general practices continue to survive in metropolitan areas where the cost of living is high and increasing numbers of twenty-four-hour emergency or specialty care hospitals might be taking away the high-end services?

Changes related to the increased specialization of veterinary medicine can be embraced as an opportunity to create a win-win scenario for general practitioners, specialists, and pet owners. Avoid any temptation to view referral practices as competition. The best medicine for pets and the best client service for owners occur by adopting a team approach to veterinary care. General practices that develop a collaborative working relationship with emergency and specialty practices do not feel like they lose money or services to the referral hospital. In fact, the opposite is true. Positive referral experiences and enhanced communication result in greater client satisfaction, better patient outcomes, and increased revenue for both practices.

When you build positive relationships with specialists based on mutual respect and understanding, you will be able to send cases to them without the fear of losing clients or revenues. Refer pet owners to hospitals where you know they will be treated well and referred back to your hospital when the emergency or need for specialty service has resolved. Communicate with referral hospitals about which services you feel comfortable providing so they know when to send cases back to your practice for continued care.

Practices that perform high-quality care and develop strong client bonds will thrive because they have already developed trust with clients. Plenty of high-end services can be done in general practices if the team stays educated and on the cutting edge of veterinary medicine. One of the best ways to stay current is to learn from specialists. Practitioners who work closely with specialists often report that they gain knowledge that helps them work up cases better and know which tests or procedures can be done prior to referral. They also find service revenue increases as a result of recommendations made by the specialist for ongoing treatment and follow-up diagnostics to be done at the general practice.

The white paper *2006–2007 AAHA Forums on Veterinarian–Veterinary Specialist Referral Issues: Report on Key Findings and Best Practices*, by Amanda L. Donnelly, DVM, MBA, is a useful resource for building positive referral relationships.

How do we maximize the effectiveness of our practice web site?

Every veterinary practice needs a web site to assist with marketing efforts, but it is no longer enough to just have a web site. To stay competitive and reap the full value of having a web site, businesses need to maximize the effectiveness of web sites as marketing tools. One of the best ways to do this is to answer questions such as "What information do our clients want?" or "Why would a client visit our web site?" or "What will our clients find of value on our web site?" Answering these questions helps to ensure the practice is leveraging the effectiveness of the web site.

First and foremost, make sure your web site is designed by a professional, has appealing graphics, and is easy to navigate. Clients need to be able to quickly find basic information, such as hospital hours, contact information, location, and a list of services. When clients visit the web site for the first time, they generally want to know more about the practice. Give pet owners specific information about the practice's philosophy, hospital facilities and equipment, scope of services, and team members so they can get a better understanding of what the practice has to offer. Use attractive, high-quality photos to enhance the visual appeal of your web site.

For web sites to be most effective, clients should find something of value. Using the hospital web site to give something of value to clients helps to attract new clients and retain current clients. Augment your client service by putting hospital forms on the web site, accepting prescription refills, and using pet portals so clients can manage their pets' health care and communicate with the practice. Post articles on health care topics and provide links to other web sites where clients can find credible information on a variety of medical topics and pet-related services or organizations. Encourage people to sign up for a monthly or quarterly e-newsletter from the practice. Engage pet owners with short videos about the practice or pet care topics and client satisfaction surveys.

Make sure that someone in the practice is responsible for keeping the web site current. It is also a good idea to change the content on a seasonal or quarterly basis. For example, you could have a calendar of local events and a section on pet care tips that change periodically.

84

Should we use social media services for our business?

Social media and social networking on the Internet have become popular ways for people to keep informed and stay connected. Some businesses and organizations now use communication applications of social media such as blogs, Facebook, Twitter, and YouTube to disseminate information and stay in touch with their target audience. As with any form of communication, there are pros and cons. On the plus side, social media can be a way to interact and build relationships with clients, create a presence that can help attract new clients, and show your willingness to create open dialogue with clients. The downside to social media is the time investment to come up with interesting content, the inability to completely control messages, and the unknown factors of whether your involvement is worthwhile or effective in marketing the practice. Social media may not be a worthwhile marketing tool, depending on the demographics of your area and your clients.

If you do decide to pursue social media outlets, make sure you develop a strategy to use social media for the business—define desired outcomes and establish a process to govern usage for your practice. It is wise to seek outside professional assistance and designate someone in the practice to monitor social networking sites. Plan ahead to decide who will be the "voice" or "face" of the hospital and who will create content to use on social media applications.

It is also a good idea to include social media policies in your employee handbook. Make sure employees know that it is not acceptable to post photos or information about the hospital on their personal accounts with social media outlets such as Facebook.

CHAPTER RESOURCES

Groups and Associations

DVM360, www.dvm360.com.

SurveyMonkey.com.

Veterinary Hospital Managers Association, Inc., www.vhma.org.

VetPartners, www.vetpartners.org. VetPartners is a national association whose membership includes experienced veterinary consultants. You can visit their web site to find a consultant to assist you with marketing.

Publications

Ackerman, Lowell, DVM, DACVD, MBA, MPA, *Blackwell's Five-Minute Veterinary Practice Management Consult* (Blackwell Publishing, 2007).

Berry, Leonard L., and Kent D. Seltman, *Management Lessons from Mayo Clinic* (McGraw-Hill, 2008).

Boss, Nan, DVM, *Educating Your Clients from A to Z* (AAHA Press, 1999).

Catanzaro, Thomas E., DVM, MHA, FACHE, *Promoting the Human-Animal Bond in Veterinary Practice* (Iowa State University Press, 2001).

Donnelly, Amanda L., DVM, MBA, *2006–2007 AAHA Forums on Veterinarian– Veterinary Specialist Referral Issues: Report on Key Findings and Best Practices.* Available at www.aahanet.org/resources/whitepapers.aspx.

Fleming, John H., and Jum Asplund, *Human Sigma* (Gallup Press, 2007).

Lagoni, Laurel, MS, and Dana Durrance, MA, *Connecting with Clients*, 2nd Edition (AAHA Press, 2010).

Smith, Carin A., DVM, *Client Satisfaction Pays: Quality Service for Practice Success*, 2nd Edition (AAHA Press, 2009).

How do I track client compliance?

One of the best ways to track compliance is to utilize your veterinary management software. Many practices don't take advantage of the options that are available to generate reports on client compliance. Your practice management software may be able to create a list of declined services, create reports that track the hospital's standards of care, and customize searches for specific service categories.

Make sure that routine reminders for services such as vaccinations, fecals, heartworm tests, and wellness examinations are entered into the computer, so you can track client response. With most practice management software, you can also create and use "recommendation" codes that are associated with specific procedures for which you want to track compliance. For example, when technicians make a dental recommendation, they enter a code for this in the computer. Then a note such as "recommend dental" will appear on the client's invoice as well as in the client computer record. A line-item report will show how many dentals were recommended, which can be cross-referenced with the number of dentals that were actually done.

In addition, you can track compliance by performing regular medical record audits at least several times a year. Random audits give you a general idea of compliance. You can pull 100 client charts, for example, and assess whether your staff made appropriate recommendations, whether the client followed through with the recommendations, and whether the clients have purchased the proper amount of preventive medications.

�III➡ **Do It Now**

Contact the company representative for your practice management software to determine the system's capabilities and to see how you can better track client compliance.

�III➡ **Do It Now**

Pull ten to twenty random client files to check the medical records for owner compliance. Determine whether the care provided matches the treatment recommendations. Calculate the percentage of compliance and discuss the results with your team.

�III➡ **Do It Now**

Adopt a policy of having certain staff members call clients who don't respond to reminders or who don't schedule recommended services. Put specific employees in charge of tracking compliance for each item you track, such as spay or neuter compliance, dental recommendations, therapeutic diet food compliance, heartworm preventive compliance, and so on.

How do I get staff to buy in to the importance of enhancing client compliance and monitor their success with making recommendations?

Training is the key to success in getting staff to buy in to the importance of enhancing client compliance. Once team members are comfortable with client education and recognize that increasing client compliance helps pets receive better care, they will do a better job with efforts to enhance client compliance with health care recommendations. The books listed at the end of this chapter are good sources for staff training on the value of compliance. AAHA's Compliance Follow-Up Study builds on AAHA's landmark 2003 study of compliance.

Make sure team members are trained to explain all the benefits and values of services and products. Use staff meetings to discuss different medical topics each month (e.g., you might talk about dentistry services in February, which is Dental Health Month). You can do role-playing to demonstrate how staff should educate clients and explain the benefits of specific services. This helps to reinforce the hospital recommendations and ensure that team members are capable of communicating those recommendations.

To monitor team members' recommendations, you can spend time in each area of the hospital listening to client interactions, and coach staff on how to improve their communication skills. Assess whether employees are striving to make appointments for recommended services before clients leave. Assign an associate veterinarian or senior staff member to mentor less experienced team members to help them learn how to effectively educate clients. Meet periodically with these individuals to discuss their progress. You can also hire individuals to be "mystery phone shoppers" or "mystery clients." Just be sure to alert the staff if you will be using this method to enhance your training and staff performance.

⁙➡ **Do It Now**

Use a checklist for wellness appointments to ensure that all relevant medical topics get discussed and appropriate recommendations are given to clients. Make it a policy that all team members are required to note health care recommendations in the medical records.

87

How do we effectively communicate with clients on financial topics?

Provide written treatment plans (a better term than "estimate") to clients in advance of services to minimize the chance of any miscommunications about fees. Educate clients about costs and their financial options during an office visit or discussion for a procedure so they can choose what is best for their family. Be sure to keep clients apprised of their bill as hospitalized cases progress. Communicate payment policies and options to pet owners before a sensitive financial situation arises.

Ideally, treatment plans should be presented by a trained staff member rather than the doctor. This takes doctors out of administrative duties and keeps them focused on medical duties. Doctors will need to be involved in fee discussions if the client cannot afford all services and services must be prioritized or alternative medical options need to be explored.

When clients react angrily about fees, listen to them without interruption and try not to be defensive. Convey empathy regarding their personal situation and reinforce the value of the services. Sometimes clients have the ability to pay for your services, but they just need to vent about the cost of medical care. When clients do have cost constraints, offer assistance by discussing payment options such as third-party payment plans. Everyone on the team needs to be trained and comfortable with interacting with emotional clients. Hold team meetings to discuss handling client reactions to fees. Do role-playing and learn from each other what has worked and not worked when interacting with emotional clients.

How do I increase client compliance in a depressed economy?

Efforts to increase client compliance, regardless of the state of the economy, should center on educating clients on health care topics and their individual pet's needs. Compliance rates generally go up when the entire veterinary team clearly communicates the value of services so clients understand the benefits for their pets. Even in a depressed economy, many people can and will spend money as long as they understand your services and why they are important for their pet.

When business is slow, practices have more time for training, and team members can often spend more time with clients. Make sure doctors and staff convey consistent messages to pet owners about the value of any medical recommendations and preventive health care. Don't assume clients cannot afford care. Promote the best medicine for each pet. You may need to offer multiple options for diagnostics and treatments for clients with cost constraints. Remember to be informative, supportive, patient, and nonjudgmental if clients don't comply with recommendations. They may just need to temporarily defer care.

Bear in mind that if you want to increase compliance, you must first conduct a compliance audit so you know your current compliance rates. Once you know how you are doing, you can set target goals to increase client compliance. Check compliance for treatments and services that you commonly perform, such as fecals, heartworm testing, preanesthetic blood work, senior testing, and dental cleanings. One step to increase compliance is to establish effective reminder protocols. Ask clients whether they want to receive written reminders, e-mails, or phone calls for routine services. Then assess which methods seem to work the best. Call clients to remind them of all appointments. Set a schedule to follow up with clients who have deferred treatment or whose pets may need ongoing care.

Ⅲ➡ **Do It Now**

Use goal setting and incentives for the team to help them with compliance and to get clients the educational information they need. An example of this would be designating a "Dental Health" quarter with goals set for the team at the start of the quarter. Track weekly or monthly dental procedures on a chart, and if the team reaches the set goals throughout the quarter, they receive their incentive, such as a staff lunch or gift cards.

How do I make sure clients receive a consistent message from all levels of the hospital team regarding medical and service excellence?

Start by setting medical and client service standards and then communicate them to the entire team. The practice owner and all veterinarians must reach consensus on medical protocols. The leadership team needs to agree on service standards to follow. Ideally, the entire staff should be involved in the process of establishing service standards; this facilitates staff buy-in, and employees are a great resource for service ideas. Once you have developed hospital standards, train employees to the standards to make sure all clients receive the same messages regarding your standards of care and service.

To be effective in giving consistent messages, provide training for the entire team. Written handbooks that outline protocols and standards are an essential training tool to educate staff. Use these handbooks to review standards with current employees, and give them to new hires to help with their training. Utilize client handouts to help team members achieve consistency with client education messages. Use CDs, DVDs, in-house seminars, and role-playing to augment staff training and ensure that the team has "one voice" when communicating with clients.

Regular departmental and general staff meetings are vital for keeping messages consistent and ensuring open communication among all team members. Discuss any situations in which the team may have fallen short of the standards. Determine whether more training is needed or you need to change protocols. When protocols do change, solicit feedback from the team regarding how best to present new information to clients.

ⅲ➡ **Do It Now**

Write one or two short quizzes to give to the team to help assess their knowledge of medical protocols or service standards. You can develop quizzes on a
variety of subjects, such as what to tell clients about heartworm prevention,
how to respond to difficult clients, nutritional recommendations for senior
pets, or the protocol for testing pets on nonsteroidal inflammatory drugs.
Use quizzes as training tools to educate staff about hospital standards and
ensure consistency of client messages.

How can we improve the effectiveness of hospital programs (e.g., wellness programs, such as dental care and senior care)?

Effective planning is the first step to improving client compliance with hospital programs. Meet with team members to assess the organization of your programs. Begin by determining whether you have protocols in place for each program. For example, protocols for a senior care program typically include setting an age at which pets receive senior care and setting minimum laboratory testing procedures such as a complete blood count, a chemistry profile, urinalysis, and a thyroid test. Additional components of the senior program can include an orthopedic evaluation, nutritional counseling, weight management, dental assessment, and additional tests such as blood pressure, as needed. For protocols to be effective, all doctors in the practice must reach consensus and everyone on the team needs to make consistent recommendations to clients.

Another critical part of organization is to ensure that you have tools in place to support your hospital programs. These can include client questionnaires, client education brochures, client report cards, visual models for exam rooms, educational articles for clients posted on your web site, hospital displays, therapeutic diet samples, adequate stock of take-home products, and a checkoff list for team members.

Once you and your team feel you have a well-organized program in place, focus on execution. To execute an effective hospital wellness program, the entire team must be involved and understand their roles in helping to enhance patient advocacy and client compliance. It can be helpful to develop a written standard operating procedure (SOP) for wellness appointments that outlines all actions taken by team members from the time the client calls for an appointment through the time of follow-up with the client and recheck visits.

Assign responsibilities for different components of the program to various team members. For example, put the front office team in charge of ensuring that clients fill out questionnaires and scheduling recheck appointments. Assign technicians to obtain lab samples and educate clients about preventive health topics such as nutrition and dental home care. Each team member needs to be properly trained to fulfill his or her specific role. One of the best methods for training is to invite industry representatives to give staff seminars and provide the practice with support materials for client education. In addition, use team meetings to discuss the consistency of client messages and any challenges that may arise for the team.

The part of the execution process that drives the success of hospital programs is follow-up with clients. Make sure you have reminder systems in place to contact clients who have pets scheduled for rechecks or on chronic medications, as well as for clients who defer treatment recommendations. Be sure to routinely call clients to ask about a pet's progress—even to check on whether the pet likes a new diet or to see how the owner is doing with dental home care.

 CHAPTER RESOURCES

Publications

Ackerman, Lowell, DVM, DACVD, MBA, MPA, *Blackwell's Five-Minute Veterinary Practice Management Consult* (Blackwell Publishing, 2007).

American Animal Hospital Association, *Compliance: Taking Quality Care to the Next Level* (AAHA Press, 2009). This 2009 AAHA Compliance Follow-Up Study builds on AAHA's landmark 2003 study of compliance. *Compliance* is the report of the findings.

American Animal Hospital Association, *Path to High-Quality Care* (AAHA Press, 2003). This is the original AAHA Compliance Study.

American Animal Hospital Association, *Six Steps to Higher-Quality Patient Care* (AAHA Press, 2009). This 2009 AAHA Compliance Follow-Up Study builds on AAHA's landmark 2003 study of compliance. *Six Steps to Higher-Quality Patient*

Care presents the study recommendations, which can be used for staff training purposes.

Wutchiett Tumblin and Associates, *Benchmarks 2008: A Study of Well-Managed Practices* (Advanstar Veterinary Healthcare Communications, 2008).

91

What are some great continuing education materials for practice managers, especially those with no previous management experience?

A number of resources are available for continuing education for both new practice managers and more experienced managers. Take advantage of continuing education seminars, books and journals, online courses, message boards and e-newsletters, networking with other managers, and coaching or mentoring offered by colleagues and consultants.

National, regional, and local veterinary conferences offer presentations and programs focused on practice management. The larger national meetings offer a greater variety of seminars over multiple days. Smaller meetings sometimes offer more intensive training on a particular topic. Evaluate your options and find the conference that is right for you. Don't forget also to explore options outside the veterinary profession. Most communities have seminars on such topics as human resource management, accounting, communication skills, customer service, and computer skills.

Several organizations in the veterinary profession offer a wide range of resources for practice managers in addition to seminars. For example, AAHA, www.aahanet.org, offers training materials and numerous practice tools in addition to their continuing education programs. Besides web-based training and in-person meetings such as those provided by the Veterinary Management Institute (VMI) (in conjunction with Purdue University), AAHA offers publications on management, including various books and *Trends* magazine, through their bookstore.

In addition, the VHMA, www.vhma.org, provides members with newsletters, survey data, mentors, and discussion boards and offers continuing education seminars and a certification program for veterinary practice managers (CVPM), as well as networking in veterinary management.

Reading journals and books on a consistent basis helps managers at all levels keep current on business topics and trends in veterinary medicine. Subscribe to those journals and e-newsletters that you find most helpful. Again, remember to look for resources outside veterinary medicine. Some excellent resources are included at the end of this chapter.

One of the best ways for managers to learn and grow is to network with managers from other veterinary practices or small businesses. Join your local managers' group for discussions and support.

Ⅲ➡ **Do It Now**

Start a list of books that you want to read on various management and business topics (see the chapter resources for a good selection). Ask colleagues and friends to recommend good books. Try to read at least one book a month.

How do I manage and prioritize my time?

Time management is a challenge for busy practice managers who often must juggle multiple job roles. You can enhance your ability to manage and prioritize your time when you are organized and effective with delegation. This affords you the opportunity to spend time on the most important job tasks rather than just reacting to situations.

Getting organized usually involves the use of some type of planner to keep track of daily, weekly, and monthly tasks or meetings. Find a planner that works for you. Some people prefer hard-copy calendars and planners, whereas others prefer electronic planners. Inevitably, daily to-do lists are unrealistic and not completed. It makes more sense to do weekly planning and assign reasonable deadlines to activities and projects, realizing that on any given day you may have to respond to the unexpected demands of a busy veterinary practice. Set aside blocks of time on your planner for daily job duties that must be completed and for job tasks that are deadline driven.

Prioritize projects or activities based on their value in achieving practice goals. For example, finalizing the budget and updating the fee schedule would take precedence over researching new interview questions for job candidates. When organizing your time, be careful not to spend too much time on activities or distractions that may seem urgent but really aren't very important. For example, limit the time spent on e-mails, phone calls, staff interruptions, and meetings that are not time sensitive.

Delegating job tasks to employees frees you up to spend time planning and working on more important job duties, such as employee development, financial management, and marketing. Don't use the excuse of being too busy to delegate or you'll never have enough time to spend on the less urgent yet important job duties.

Stephen Covey's book, *The 7 Habits of Highly Successful People* (Simon & Schuster, 1989), is an excellent resource to learn more about effective time management.

How do I divide my time if I perform other duties in the hospital as well?

Time management is even more challenging for practice managers who also have job duties as part of the technical team or at the front desk with the client service representatives. To be successful, establish clear job expectations with the practice owner and the rest of the team so you can stay focused on the job duties you are performing. Try to avoid being pulled in multiple directions all the time. You also need to set up an effective work schedule and prioritize your job responsibilities.

Try to designate specific times to complete management duties, and avoid interruptions. Give staff a written schedule so they know when you are available and where you will be working each day. Work with the owner and team members to agree on reasonable time lines and deadlines to complete projects.

Prioritize your job tasks each day so you can attend to time-sensitive or urgent matters first. Learn to say no if you are asked to take on work that is not part of your job description or is less critical. Finish duties that must be completed that day first, and then work on your most important projects next. Part of your prioritization process should involve delegation of duties to other team members. When you delegate effectively, you have more time to spend in areas of management that may not seem urgent but are vital to the success of the practice, such as financial management, marketing, and employee development. Finally, consider talking to the practice owner about making your manager position full-time. It may not be realistic for you to manage the practice and perform job duties in other areas. Explain to the owner that you will be more effective at managing the hospital if you have more time.

How can I encourage team members to respect my privacy and space when my office door is closed?

Clearly communicate to the staff when you are available and when you need uninterrupted time to work on projects or hold meetings. Tell staff what it means when your door is closed. Also, offer appointment times to staff members who need time to talk, and be sure to set aside plenty of time when you are readily available to the staff.

It can be helpful to post a sign on the office door when you wish not to be interrupted along with the times when you will be available again. The sign can be a dry erase board or memo for you to write down what you are doing behind the door (i.e., working on budget, paying bills, working on protocols, and so forth). This alleviates any tension or fear that you are doing something secret or disciplining an employee. Some managers have found that using a sign with a fun picture or something amusing on it with a statement that there is a meeting in progress has helped eliminate interruptions.

Establish a protocol for interruptions in the event that a team member absolutely must speak to you. Instruct staff that a closed door or the presence of someone in your office means you need to be uninterrupted and they should knock if their need is urgent. Train the team to take a message and tell callers that you are in a meeting if the door is closed. If a situation arises for which that is not feasible, employees can reach you via the intercom and explain the situation.

How do I handle my frustration and anger at mistakes that staff members make?

Think of "responding" to staff mistakes in an appropriate manner rather than "reacting" inappropriately. Avoid negative reactions or comments to staff that you will later regret. If you react rather than respond, then you have lost control of the situation and you risk losing the respect and trust of your team. Delay your response to a situation that is frustrating. It may be helpful to go to your office, take a walk, or call a colleague in order to collect your thoughts about how you want to respond. Sometimes mistakes are unavoidable or occur by accident. After you have taken time to reflect on the mistake, you can decide what steps, if any, are necessary to take with the employee. Write notes about the incident and how you want to calmly respond to your staff, which will help you focus on the behavior you want to correct rather than your emotions.

Before taking any action regarding employee mistakes, seek to understand the underlying reason for the mistake. Could it be a result of miscommunication, poor training, or confusion about protocols? Is the mistake a result of poor attention to detail or lack of accountability due to a poor attitude? Then schedule a meeting with the employee to discuss the problem. Consider the facts and feedback from the employee so you can take appropriate action steps to prevent the mistake from happening again. Look for ways to turn mistakes into productive learning opportunities. Ask whether the employee has ideas on how to correct the situation, and engage the employee in correcting the mistake, if possible. Often, staff have some good ideas on how to change things to prevent mistakes. When mistakes happen repeatedly with the same employee, however, you need to address the underlying cause, work on a specific plan to increase accountability, and be willing to discipline or terminate the employee if his or her job performance doesn't improve.

Don't forget that if your frustration with the team member shows, apologize!

⟹ **Do It Now**

Make the most of local practice managers' groups. This is a great place to voice your frustrations. If you have a group in your area, join now! If you don't have one, then take steps to start one. Call a few managers from other area practices and set up an initial meeting to get started. You can use the VHMA as a resource because it maintains a list of local managers with contact information. Call one of these individuals or post on the listserv to get ideas about organizing a managers' group in your area.

How do I help multiple partners or owners make concrete decisions in a timely manner and still keep the peace?

Working in a practice with multiple owners can be a challenge for managers if the partners don't agree on how the practice should be managed or if they are slow to make decisions. Open lines of communication are a must if you have more than one owner. Set up regular leadership meetings and establish protocols for decision making. Let owners know when their action or their failure to take action hinders your job performance.

Opening lines of communication includes getting owners to agree on the vision, core values, and goals for the practice. This helps set the foundation for decision making. Making decisions should be quicker and easier if everyone stays focused on doing what is best for the success of the business. As a manager, your role in keeping the peace is to remind owners to make decisions aligned with hospital goals and core values.

During leadership meetings, facilitate timely decision making by owners by suggesting actions or solutions that clearly benefit the practice. Always try to get owners to agree to deadlines for making decisions if you can't get them to agree on action items at the meeting. Prioritize the meeting agenda as well so that failure to make decisions on the most important items doesn't occur just because you ran out of time for discussion.

Another protocol that can help with decision making is to get owners to individually agree to oversight of specific areas of the hospital or specific areas of management. Then it may not be necessary to achieve consensus from multiple owners for every decision. For example, you may check with one owner regarding inventory issues and another owner regarding employee accountability problems. All aspects of management still need to be discussed during leadership meetings, but minor issues or problems can be addressed on a daily basis without having to seek approval from multiple owners.

How do I maintain respect among team members when the owner does not remember, support, or model directives he or she wishes me to develop or uphold?

It can be difficult to maintain respect and accountability with the team if the practice owner does not follow hospital policies and model the behavior that the manager is expected to uphold and enforce. If this is an issue, assess your communication with the practice owner. Start by having an honest conversation—explain that you need the owner's full support, and give specific examples of instances where this has not happened. Talk about the importance of presenting a united front to the team, and emphasize that staff become confused if they hear mixed messages or see inconsistent behaviors from the leadership team. Make sure you have a commitment from the owner for a change in behavior before you leave the meeting, which you can reference later if necessary.

Next, ensure open lines of communication by requesting weekly meetings with the owner. Document conversations related to hospital directives. Be sure to present any directives you are implementing along with the reasons for the directives, who will be involved in implementation, and how the directives will benefit the practice. If the owner cannot make weekly meetings, provide a detailed weekly written report and request approval for any new directives.

Once you have an established communication protocol in place with the owner, assess your communication with the team. Remind the staff of their roles in accomplishing the practice's goals. Focus team members on their behavior and the need to model the proper behavior. Be careful not to be drawn into discussions about the owner's behavior, and refrain from complaining about the owner's lack of support.

If the owner continues to undermine your efforts, explain that you cannot successfully fulfill your job duties as a manager. If the owner still does not support you, then it may be time to look for another job.

98

How do I create a balance between maintaining a friendly work environment and adhering to policies and procedures without sounding threatening on the one hand or being taken advantage of on the other?

Managers must find a balance between being friendly with employees and at the same time fostering a professional workplace. A friendly atmosphere does not mean that the manager is friends with all the team members. Employees appreciate and respect managers who are fair, are consistent with policy enforcement, are open to feedback, and can build rapport with their team.

Make sure the staff is well informed of the practice's policies and the reasons behind them. Team members need to understand that policies and procedures are designed to improve the practice in some way. This may be by improving patient care, client communication, safety, operational efficiency, or staff relations, or by meeting legal requirements. When employees buy in to the importance of policies and procedures, adherence to protocols will increase.

Use tools to make sure employees have a clear understanding of what is expected. An employee manual is essential to outline and detail in writing some of the most important policies. Written job expectations and a professional code of conduct for all employees also help set the foundation for adherence to procedures and protocols.

Maintain consistency when enforcing policies. Avoid favoritism and demonstrate respect for staff by asking for feedback and listening before taking any disciplinary action. A positive work environment can be maintained by keeping open lines of communication and by creating a culture of consistent praise and appreciation.

When inappropriate behavior occurs, talk to the involved employee in private. The conversation does not need to be threatening; instead, it should have more of an open and encouraging tone.

Effective staff communication is honest and clear. Focus on the employee's job performance or behavior and give specific examples of how he or she failed to adhere to hospital policies.

Remind the team of their role in fulfilling the practice's goals, core values, and vision. Employees are much more receptive to dialogue focused on core values and vision than to nagging about failure to adhere to policies. Finally, remember to lead by example. Managers must follow established hospital policies and procedures.

How do I ensure that hospital policies are followed when I'm not there?

If you want to ensure that hospital policies are followed, start by being certain that everyone on the team is familiar with all policies. Verify that each employee has acknowledged receipt of the employee manual or other documents outlining hospital protocols. Review policies with all new hires and address any new or amended policies during regular staff meetings. Discussing the reasons behind the policies helps staff understand why specific policies have been put in place and affords them an opportunity to ask questions.

To ensure everyone adheres to policies, even when you are not at the hospital, appoint team leaders or supervisors to oversee operations in your absence. Delegate this responsibility to employees who are trusted and respected. Make sure all staff members and veterinarians know who is in charge when you are away. Team leaders need to be trained and empowered to handle situations requiring immediate attention. Most personnel issues can be brought to your attention and addressed upon your return to the practice.

Strive to create a culture of accountability, trust, and respect. In a culture with these core values, employees take ownership for their behavior and are more likely to follow policies because they want to, not because someone is looking over their shoulders. Staff members tend to resent managers who are authoritative and quick to discipline. If an employee fails to follow a hospital policy, always ask why before taking any action. You may uncover relevant information and have an opportunity to coach the employee on the value of policies. Then you can give the employee feedback on how he or she must be accountable in the future.

100

What do I do if an employee doesn't respect my authority?

Sometimes a manager may have difficulty gaining the respect of employees who resent that the manager has been promoted from within. Or the manager may be younger than the team members, have less tenure than long-term employees, or be faced with handling an employee with a bad attitude. Regardless of the scenario, managers will not be as effective if team members don't respect their authority. When faced with this situation, you need first to make sure you have the support and backing of the practice owner. Otherwise you will be fighting an uphill battle to try to gain the respect of team members.

Assuming the employee who demonstrates a lack of respect is a valued team member, strive to iron out any differences and foster a professional working relationship. Make sure the employee understands how his or her behavior may be damaging to morale, may create negativity that can decrease productivity, or may interfere with client service and prevent you from being an effective manager. Seek to understand the employee's position. Maybe the employee feels underappreciated or simply doesn't understand your management style. Often, open dialogue can help bridge the gap in communication and lead to an improved relationship.

If employees don't respect your decisions or they act in inappropriate ways, remind them of the importance of teamwork to achieve the practice's mission or vision. Assure them that your actions are to further the practice's goals and you need their help. In addition, refer to the practice's core values or code of conduct to guide behavior. Let the employees know if their actions aren't consistent with the core values. Discussing the mission and core values of the business is more meaningful than just demanding automatic respect.

If, despite all your efforts, an employee still refuses to be a team player and act professionally, you may need to take disciplinary action and consider termination of that employee.

101

How can I "manage up" effectively?

The term "managing up" or "managing your boss" has many definitions and is not always clearly understood. In their article "Managing Your Boss," Thomas J. Zuber, MD, and Erika H. James, PhD, define managing up as "the process of consciously working with your boss to obtain the best possible results for you, your boss, and your organization." Managing up doesn't mean you are "kissing up" or trying to manipulate your boss. It is about building a positive working relationship that will allow you to be a more effective manager and assist in furthering the practice's goals.

Managers who are good at managing up have a clear understanding of their job roles, their strengths and weaknesses, and their communication style. They also understand their boss's perspective and management style, to which they are flexible and adaptive. For example, if you know your boss hates tardiness and likes to hear factual information, you will make sure you are never late to meetings and always present data to support suggested hospital expenditures or changes in policy.

For managing up to be effective, you must meet regularly with your practice owner. Review priorities with respect to job assignments and hospital goals. Clarify job expectations when needed. Ask for feedback from the practice owner regarding your job performance so you know what you are doing well and where you need to improve.

Build trust with the practice owner by being accountable and showing your commitment to the hospital vision. Demonstrate your leadership by always proposing solutions to problems when discussing hospital challenges. By communicating effectively and building trust with the owner, you will increase your value as a manager and help make the practice more successful.

CHAPTER RESOURCES

Groups and Associations

American Animal Hospital Association (AAHA), www.aahanet.org. AAHA's bookstore offers a great number of books and *Trends* magazine to help practice managers succeed, and AAHA periodically offers a Veterinary Leadership Workshop and in-person and web-based meetings, such as the Veterinary Management Institute.

DVM360, www.veterinaryteam.dvm360.com. Through this web site, you can subscribe to *Veterinary Economics* magazine, which contains articles and resources on a variety of management topics.

Exceptional Veterinary Team, www.myevt.com.

Society for Human Resource Management (SHRM), www.shrm.org. SHRM is a comprehensive resource for human resource management and offers articles, publications, conferences, tools, and forms on a variety of topics.

Veterinary Emergency & Specialty Practice Association (VESPA), www.vesp association.org. This association is helpful for managers at referral practices. VESPA has discussion forums, monthly chat sessions, and other tools for referral practices.

Veterinary Hospital Managers Association (VHMA), www.vhma.org. VHMA offers education, certification, and networking in veterinary management.

VetPartners, www.vetpartners.org. VetPartners is a national association whose membership includes experienced veterinary consultants. Their web site offers a list of consultants to help you with many areas of practice development.

Publications

Ackerman, Lowell, DVM, DACVD, MBA, MPA, *Blackwell's Five-Minute Veterinary Practice Management Consult* (Blackwell Publishing, 2007).

Alessandra, Tony, *The Platinum Rule: Discover the Four Basic Business Personalities and How They Can Lead You to Success* (Warner Business Books, 1998).

American Animal Hospital Association, *AAHA Guide to Creating an Employee Handbook*, Third Edition (AAHA Press, 2009).

Badowski, Rosanne, and Roger Gittines, *Managing Up: How to Forge an Effective Relationship with Those Above You* (Doubleday Business, 2003).

Blanchard, Ken, *Empowerment Takes More Than a Minute,* Second Edition (Berrett-Koehler, 2001).

Blanchard, Ken, *The One Minute Manager* (Berkley Trade, 1986).

Blanchard, Ken, *The One Minute Manager Builds High Performing Teams* (William Morrow, 1991).

Blanchard, Ken, William Oncken, and Hal Burrows, *The One Minute Manager Meets the Monkey* (William Morrow, 1991).

Buckingham, Marcus, and Curt Coffman Buckingham, *First Break All the Rules: What the World's Greatest Managers Do Differently* (Simon & Schuster, 1999).

Covey, Stephen R., *The 7 Habits of Highly Successful People* (Simon & Schuster, 1989).

Flaherty, James, *Coaching: Evoking Excellence in Others*, Second Edition (Butterworth-Heinemann, 2005).

Heinke, Marsha L., DVM, EA, CPA, CVPM, and John B. McCarthy, DVM, MBA, *Practice Made Perfect* (AAHA Press, 2001).

Lee, Fred, *If Disney Ran Your Hospital* (Second River Healthcare, 2004).

Lundin, Stephen C., Harry Paul, and John Christensen, *Fish* (Hyperion, 2000).

Maxwell, John C., *21 Indispensable Qualities of a Leader*, Second Edition (Thomas Nelson, 2007).

Miller, Brian Cole, *Keeping Employees Accountable for Results* (American Management Association, 2006).

Morgenstern, Julie, *Time Management from the Inside Out*, Second Edition (Holt Paperbacks, 2004).

Smith, Carin A., DVM, *Team Satisfaction Pays: Organizational Development for Practice Success* (Smith Veterinary Consulting, 2009).

Takash, Joe, *Results Through Relationships: Building Trust, Performance, and Profit Through People* (Wiley, 2008).

Zuber, Thomas J., MD, and Erika H. James, PhD, "Managing Your Boss," in *Family Practice Management*, June 2001, pp. 33–36. Available at http://penfm.pbworks.com/f/Manage-your-boss.pdf.

Courses

Firstline, www.dvm360.com. You can subscribe to *Firstline* magazine and sign up for Firstline seminars, which are offered at the CVC conferences.

Veterinary Management Consultation, School of Veterinary Practice Management, www.vmc-inc. VMC offers a five-day training course for practice managers in Denver, Colorado.

Veterinary Management Institute (VMI), http://www.aahanet.org/education/vmi.aspx. VMI is a comprehensive, "mini-MBA" program for veterinary professionals offered by AAHA and Purdue University. The program has management modules: human resource management, financial management, marketing management, and strategic thinking.

Veterinary Specialists in Private Practice (VSIPP), www.vsipp.com. VSIPP holds an annual meeting for specialty practices that offers seminars, discussion groups, workshops, and plenty of time for networking.

Veterinary Support Personnel Network (VSPN), www.vspn.org. VSPN offers discussion boards and continuing education on management topics.

VetMedTeam, www.vetmedteam.com. VetMedTeam offers some online courses in practice management.

LIST OF CONTRIBUTORS

Abbysinian, Diane C., LVN, Bond Animal Hospital, White Plains, NY

Acosta, Anjenette, Office Manager, Aztec Animal Clinic, Albuquerque, NM

Alger, Sarah, Patterson Veterinary Hospital, Patterson, CA

Alimossy, Dyana, CVT, Riverside Park Veterinary Clinic, Grants Pass, OR

Andalman, Denise, Metairie Small Animal Hospital, Inc., Metairie, LA

Angel, Belen, CVT, MBA, Apollo Animal Hospital, Glendale, AZ

April, Karen, CVT, Hospital Manager, Norton Animal Hospital, Inc., Norton, MA

Arce, Jennifer, Practice Manager, Desert Veterinary Clinic, Yuma, AZ

Arnold, Cheryl, Practice Manager, Veterinary Medical Center, Easton, MD

Arp, Dana, Bay Creek Animal Clinic, League City, TX

Ash, Becky, Dumfries Animal Hospital, Dumfries, VA

Aubin, Stacey, Bay Porte Animal Hospital, La Porte, TX

Bailey, Shari, RVT, Practice Manager, Michigan City Animal Hospital, Michigan City, IN

Baker, Donna, New River Animal Hospital, Nimitz, WV

Ball, April, Milton Animal Hospital, Milton, FL

Baran, Polly, Lakewood Animal Hospital, Lakewood, OH

Barker, Cathryn, LVT, Practice Manager, Valley Veterinary Hospital, Fargo, ND

Barley, Reba M., Office Manager, Linden Heights Animal Hospital, Winchester, VA

Barlow, Beth, RVT, Newport Harbor Animal Hospital, Costa Mesa, CA

Barr, Sheila J., LVT, Orchard Park Veterinary Medical Center, Orchard Park, NY

Barrett, Jan, RVT, CVPM, Animal Emergency Clinic, St. Louis, MO

Barth, Mary, Hospital Administrator, Village Veterinary Clinic, Knoxville, TN

Barton, Sonya D., Vinton Veterinary Hospital, Vinton, VA

Batagower, David, Sugar Land Veterinary Specialists, Sugar Land, TX

Bates, Karen, Alexandria Animal Hospital, Alexandria, VA

Bauer, Marisa, CVT, Anderson Lakes Animal Hospital, Eden Prairie, MN, and Florida Veterinary Specialists, Brandon, FL

Bauman, Donna, CVPM, Ottawa Animal Hospital, Holland, MI

Bayliff, Angie, East Central Veterinarian Hospital, Wichita, KS

Beier, Deborah, Hospital Manager, CVT, Lamoille Valley Veterinary Hospital, Hyde Park, VT

Bergeron, Pam, RVT, CVPM, University Veterinary Hospital & Diagnostic Center, Salt Lake City, UT

Bishop, Pamela, Ocean City Animal Hospital, Ocean City, MD

Bolling, Cheri, BA, CVT, AA Small Animal Emergency Service, Lexington, KY

Bordelon, Kristin, CVT, K-M Regional Veterinary Hospital and Surgical Center, Kasson, MN

Bracken-Penley, Karen, Hospital Administrator, Great Falls Animal Hospital, Great Falls, VA

Bradford, Julie, Hospital Administrator, Animal Hospital of Worthington, Worthington, OH

Bradley, Ann, Practice Manager, CVT, Cat Care Clinic, Madison, WI

Brobst, Pat, Lehigh Valley Animal Hospital, Ltd, Allentown, PA

Brown, Lori A., Night Shift Manager, Loomis Basin Veterinary Hospital, Loomis, CA

Brownson, Lori, Scott County Animal Hospital, Eldridge, IA

Bundesmann, Andrea, Hospital Administrator, Huntington Veterinary Hospital, Monrovia, CA

Burns, Kat, Director of Veterinary Services, Humane Society of Boulder Valley, Boulder, CO

Callahan, Shawn, Animal Hospital of Dunedin, Dunedin, FL

Camilo, Paul, CVPM, All Pets Dental, Weston, FL

Cascade Veterinary Center, PS, Marysville, WA

Chodrow, Ruth E., VMD, Shenandoah Valley Regional Veterinary Emergency Services, Verona, VA

Connally, Jamie, Stonebrook Veterinary Clinic, Frisco, TX

Cornprobst, Cheri, LVT, Practice Manager and Owner, Heritage Animal Hospital, Dundee, MI

Costin, Georgeta, Hospital Manager, Los Feliz Small Animal Hospital, Los Angeles, CA

Craig, Gayle Marie, CVPM, Countryside Veterinary Hospital, Chelmsford, MA

Crockett, Susie, Eagle Creek Animal Clinic, Indianapolis, IN

Cunningham, Roxanne, LVT, VCA Lewis Animal Hospital, Columbia, MD

Davidson, Sarah, Practice Manager, Dallas County Veterinary Hospital, Mesquite, TX

Davis, Jamie A., CVPM, Coal Creek Veterinary Hospital, Centennial, CO

Davis, Sharon, CVT, Sun City Animal Hospital, Sun City, AZ

de Veer, Diana, CVPM, Brandt Veterinary Clinic, Nokomis, FL

DeDeo, Joseph, Upstate Veterinary Specialties, Latham, NY

DeLucia, Theresa, Valley Animal Hospital, Clifton, NJ

Demetropolis, Stephanie, Oquirrh Hills Veterinary Center, Herriman, UT

Detrick, Melissa, BS, Honey Brook Animal Hospital, Honey Brook, PA

Dillon-Sauer, Gretchen, CVPM, South Carolina Veterinary Emergency Care, Columbia, SC

D'Souza, David, Animal Medical Center, Van Nuys, CA

Duda, Heather, BS, Gamble Pet Clinic, Fort Collins, CO

Dunn, Louise S., Snowgoose Veterinary Management Consulting, Greensboro, NC

Eagan, Michele, Practice Manager, Melrose Animal Clinic, Melrose, MA

Eagle, Tricia, MBA, Ashby Animal Clinic, Inc., Harrisonburg, VA

Edwards, Jim, Country Friends Veterinary Clinic, Terrell, TX

Egerton, Margie, Washington Park Veterinary Clinic, PC, Denver, CO

Ellis, Dawn M., CVT, SC Veterinary Specialists, Columbia, SC

Erickson, Kimberly, PHR, CVPM, Lakeland Veterinary Hospital, Baxter, MN

Erika, CVT, Wiseman Animal Hospital, Tucson, AZ

Estrada, Regina, RVT, Los Angeles, CA

Everhart, Sherry, CVT, The McCormick Consultant Group, Boalsburg, PA

Ewing, Nichole, Heartwood Animal Hospital, Youngsville, NC

Fabian, Pamela, MSW, French Creek Veterinary Hospital, Pottstown, PA

Fisher, Billie Jo, CVT, Wisconsin Veterinary Referral Center, Waukesha, WI

Focareta, James, Dr. Domotor's Animal House, Monrovia, CA

Fonseca, Kathleen B., MBA, Towne North Animal Hospital, San Antonio, TX

Fountain, Cindy, Hospital Manager, Frey Pet Hospital, Cedar Rapids, IA

Fritzler, Elizabeth, DVM, CVPM, Lien Animal Clinic, Seattle, WA

Gadek, Carrie, Hospital Manager, Animal Care Clinic, El Sobrante, CA

Gatz, Cindy, Practice Manager, Broadway Veterinary Clinic, Leavenworth, KS

Gibbs, Ellen, Snohomish Animal Hospital, Snohomish, WA

Gilbert, Juli, LVT, Orchard Hills Animal Hospital, Washougal, WA

Grantham, Linda, Practice Manager, Ellisville Veterinary Hospital, Ellisville, MO

Greenawalt, Teresa D., Office Manager, Creekwood Veterinary Hospital, Friendswood, TX

Groff, Kelly, Greenfields Veterinary Associates, LLC, Mantua, NJ

Groves, Judy, Providence Veterinary Associates, Charlotte, NC

Grycowski, Barb, CVPM, Crawford Animal Hospital, Greenfield, WI

Gulley, Adrienne R., Animal Hospital of Salinas, Salinas, CA

Hack, Peggy, Clifton-Centreville Animal Clinic, Centreville, VA

Hagedorn, Jim, DVM, Diplomate ABVP, Hospital Director, Bramer Animal Hospital Ltd., Evanston, IL

Hallback, Patti, North Shore Veterinary Hospital, Duluth, MN

Hanks, Kendra, RVT, Dakota Hills Veterinary Clinic, Rapid City, SD

Harnish, Brian, Animal Medical Center of East County, El Cajon, CA

Harvey, Beth Ann, BS, MS, CVPM, Butler Veterinary Associates, Inc., Butler, PA

Haugland, Gail, Faust Animal Hospital, Phoenix, AZ

Hayes, Tania, Blum Animal Hospital, Chicago, IL

Hedding, Stefanie, Practice Manager, Westarbor Animal Hospital, Ann Arbor, MI

Henderson, Karen, Hospital Manager, Hanover Regional Animal Hospital, Wilmington, NC

Herrild, Janice E., Town & Country Veterinary Clinic, Marinette, WI

Hester, Mary, Hospital Administrator, PetMed, Antioch, TN

Hill, Debbie, CVPM, Animal Hospital of Pensacola, Pensacola, FL

Hoffman, Kristen, BS, Veterinary Imaging Center, Ambler, PA

Holschbach, Chanda, CVT, Hospital Administrator, Packerland Veterinary Center, Green Bay, WI

Horton, Joanne, Somers Point Veterinary Hospital, Somers Point, NJ

Hueser, Jill, Johnson County Animal Clinic, Overland Park, KS

Hunt, Patricia, Practice Manager, Greenfield Animal Hospital, Miami, FL

Ikerd, Christine, Acres North Animal Hospital, San Antonio, TX

Inbody, Jennifer, CVPM, PHR, Lead Dog Consultants, Inc., Granbury, TX

Jackson, Judi, Centerville Animal Hospital, PC, Snellville, GA

Johnson, Shelley, CVPM, Animal Clinic, Inc., Grand Rapids, MI

Johnson, Vicki, CVT, Blue Cross Animal Hospital, Minneapolis, MN

Jones, Connie, B.S.Ed., Brandywine Hospital for Pets, Zanesville, OH

Juriga, Alexandra, Hospital Administrator, River Heights Veterinary Clinic, Oswego, IL

Kanter, Debbie, Blum Animal Hospital, Chicago, IL

Keller, Christina, CVPM, Lansdowne Veterinary Clinic & Dental Center, Lexington, KY

Kelley, Jodi, Practice Manager, Sauk Prairie Small Animal Hospital, Prairie du Sac, WI

Kelly, Nichole, CVT, CVPM, Raintree Animal Hospital, Fort Collins, CO

Knauf-Jackson, Lisa, Practice Manager, Stone Veterinary Hospital, Watertown, CT

Kocsis, Cathy, Office Manager, West Mountain Animal Hospital, Bennington, VT

Kolker, Shannon, Friendship Veterinary Hospital, Fort Walton Beach, FL

Krug, Penny, CVPM, Beechwold Veterinary Hospital, Inc., Columbus, OH

Kuchera, Cheryl A., Practice Manager, Pewaukee Veterinary Service, Pewaukee, WI

Lassiter, Susan, CVPM, All Creatures Animal Hospital.

Ledezma, Katie, CVA, Windhaven Veterinary Hospital, Plano, TX

Littell, Linda, RN, MBA, CVPM, West Frederick Veterinary Hospital, Frederick, MD

Lobdell, Laurie, LVT, BAS, Pet Authority Animal Hospital, Waterford, MI

Loftis, Jonathan, RVT, Central Carolina Community College, Sanford, NC

Logas, Jeffrey, BS, MS, ABD, Pet Medical Center, Winona, MN

Lord, Debbie, Practice Manager, Winder Animal Hospital, Winder, GA

Lutz, Rosanne, Office Manager, Plantation Animal Hospital, Hilton Head Island, SC

Maedke, Connie, CVT, Practice Manager, Animal Hospital of DePere, DePere, WI

Maglio, Alison Lee, Hospital Administrator, Oradell Animal Hospital Inc., Paramus, NJ

Magnifico, Richard, HA, MBA, Jarrettsville Veterinary Center, Jarrettsville, MD

Maki, Sue, CVT, Animal Wellness Center, Maple Grove, MN

Martinez, Alora, RVT, The Ark Pet Hospital, Inc., Antioch, CA

Mason, Eloise Pierson, Peaks View Animal Hospital, Lynchburg, VA

Mattacchione, Lauren, Animal Medical of Chesapeake, Chesapeake, VA

Matthews, Jenny, CVT, Doubletree Veterinary Clinic, Little Rock, AR

Matushevski, Cheryl, RT, Apple Hill Animal Hospital, Inc., Broadview Heights, OH

McCabe, Lauri, Parker Road Animal Hospital, Houston, TX

McCloskey, Carrie, Society Hill Veterinary Hospital, Philadelphia, PA

McElhinney, Kelly, MBA, Pet Medical Center & Spa, Fresno, CA

McGuire, Brad, Practice Manager, Makai Animal Clinic, Kailua, HI

McKay, Penny, West Flamingo Animal Hospital, Las Vegas, NV

McLean, Christy White, Practice Manager, The Animal Hospital of Waynesville, Waynesville, NC

Melton, Zachary, Practice Manager, Community Pet Hospital, Thornton, CO

Mercurio, Jacqueline, CVT, Holden Veterinary Clinic, Holden, MA

Merolla, Donna, Southwick Animal Hospital, Southwick, MA

Merritt, Jessie, Practice Manager, Oswego Veterinary Hospital, Lake Oswego, OR

Miller, Pamela, RVT, Dunwoody Animal Hospital, Dunwoody, GA

Miller-Drake, Lys, Practice Manager, Animal Medical Center of Chicago, Chicago, IL

Minacapelli, Cyndy, Hospital Administrator, Animal Emergency Center, Inc., Towson, MD

Miyamoto, Jernel, Aloha Animal Hospital, Honolulu, HI

Moffa, Maria A., MS, JD, Sanford Animal Hospital, Sanford, NC

Mooney-Osborne, Allegra, Maple Run Veterinary Clinic LLC, Mount Gilead, OH

Morozov, Margaret, Animal Hospital of Sussex County, Augusta, NJ

Morris, Amanda, MBA, Care Animal Hospital, Muncie, IN

Moser, Karina, MA, RVT, Charlotte Street Animal Hospital, Asheville, NC

Murphy, Holly, Companions Animal Hospital, St. Cloud, MN

Murphy, Katherine, Companion Animal Wellness Center, Poulsbo, WA

Murphy, Maggie, Highland Animal Hospital, Needham, MA

Nagle, Teresa, CVT, Practice Manager, Animal ER of University Park, Bradenton, FL

Nyvold, Fawn, Hospital Administrator and Owner, All Creatures Emergency Center, Newhall, CA

Olson, Laura, McAbee Veterinary Hospital, Winter Park, FL

Ornelas, Leslie, Practice Manager, Westside Animal Hospital, Colorado Springs, CO

Ortiz, Deb, Hospital Manager, Pacifica Pet Hospital, Pacifica, CA

Palmer, Casey, Cat Hospital Eastern Shore, Cordova, MD

Pattyn, Eve M., Practice Manager, Northside Veterinary Hospital, Muskegon, MI

Peretti, Jodi, Amherst Animal Hospital, Butte, MT

Pernot, Nikki, McFarland Animal Hospital, McFarland, WI

Perry, Jennifer, All About Pets Animal Care, Union City, CA

Pitts, Kathy, Hospital Administrator, Animal Medical Center of Cumming, Cumming, GA

Poll, Janna, MBA, SPHR, Veterinary Referral Center of Colorado, Englewood, CO

Pounds, Deb, Hoschton Animal Hospital, Hoschton, GA

Preston, Sarah, Orange Veterinary Hospital, Orange, CA

Price, Mandy, Ingleside Animal Hospital, Phoenix, AZ

Prowse, Susan, CVPM, University Animal Hospital, Tempe, AZ

Pulice, Joanne H., MBA, Perkiomen Animal Hospital, Palm, PA

Racz, Erica, Parkview Veterinary Hospital, Monterey, CA

Remick, Cindy, CVPM, Edmonds Veterinary Hospital, Edmonds, WA

Richmond, Carl, Practice Manager, Gulf Lake Animal Hospital, Richland, MI

Riddick, Don, PMP, Esq., Benning Animal Hospital, Columbus, GA

Riley, Lisha, LVT, Practice Manager, Southgate Veterinary Hospital, Fargo, ND

Rizzo, Cheryl, Ocean State Veterinary Specialists, East Greenwich, RI

Rowan, Julie, Practice Manager, Carver Lake Veterinary Center, Woodbury, MN

Royer, Allison, Liverpool Village Animal Hospital, Liverpool, NY

Ruggerone, Stephanie, Practice Administrator, Animal Care Clinic, San Luis Obispo, CA

Rusk, Joseph, CVT, VCA Animal Referral & Emergency Center of
  Arizona, Mesa, AZ

Russell, Catherine, Best Care Pet Hospital, Omaha, NE

Rutz, Melanie, Burlington Veterinary Center, Burlington, CT

Sanders, Shirley, VPM, Grayling Hospital for Animals and The
  Roscommon Veterinary Clinic, Grayling, MI

Sansinena, Lory, The Cat Doctor Veterinary Hospital & Hotel, Boise,
  ID

Saxon, Denise, CVT, MBA, Powell Blvd. Veterinary Clinic, Portland,
  OR

Schaefer, Keri Dee, Hollywood Animal Hospital, Hollywood, FL

Schaperjahn, David, Practice Manager, Burnt Hills Veterinary
  Hospital, Burnt Hills, NY

Schenck, Ken, DVM, Mueller Pet Medical Center, Sacramento, CA

Schmidt, Mary, CVT, Truesdell Animal Care Hospital, Madison, WI

Schulkey, Rick, Practice Manager, Madison Veterinary Hospital,
  Madison Heights, MI

Schumacher, Chris, Practice Manager, CPA, Cedarburg Veterinary
  Clinic, Cedarburg, WI

Schwerdt, Shelley, Practice Manager, Cottage Lake Veterinary
  Hospital, Woodinville, WA

Scibelli, Christine, AAS, RVT, Clairmont Animal Hospital, Decatur,
  GA

Sergent, Alli, LVT, Las Vegas Animal Emergency Hospital, Las Vegas,
  NV

Sharp, Denise, Olney–Sandy Spring Veterinary Hospital, Sandy
  Spring, MD

Sheppard, Karol, Wakulla County Animal Hospital, Crawfordville, FL

Shirley, Angie, Porter County Pet Clinic, Valparaiso, IN

Simmons, Karen, CPA, Wrightsville Beach Pet Hospital, Wilmington,
  NC

Smith, Belinda P., Emory Animal Hospital, Powell, TN

Smith, Kris, CVPM, Valley Animal Hospital & Pet Resort, Huntsville,
  AL

Smith, Vickie, CVPM, Lebanon Small Animal Clinic, Lebanon, OH

Snyder-Downey, Tricia, Medical Director, Colerain Animal Clinic, Cincinnati, OH

Solar, Marge, Animal Medical Centre of Medina, Medina, OH

Spangler, Deborah K., Office Manager, Animal Medical Center of Somerset County, Inc., Somerset, PA

Spencer, Christine, Hospital Administrator, The Drake Center for Veterinary Care, Encinitas, CA

Spencer, Margit, Mueller Pet Medical Center, Sacramento, CA

Sprague, Barbara, Beach Park Animal Hospital, Beach Park, IL

Stamberger, Christina, Bay Cities Veterinary Hospital, Marina del Rey, CA

Stephens, Julia, BA, Muller Veterinary Hospital, Walnut Creek, CA

Stephens, Sandra G., RVT, Shenandoah Veterinary Hospital Inc., Martinsburg, WV

Sternberg, Juliet, LMSW, Hope Veterinary Clinic, Brooklyn, NY

Stouffer, Lynne, Brook-Falls Veterinary Hospital & Exotic Care Inc., Brookfield, WI

Strom, Randie, Kitty Hawk Animal Hospital, Universal City, TX

Suazo, Stacey, Pecan Acres Pet Care, Clute and Lake Jackson, TX

Sullivan, Tom, Hospital Administrator, Town & Country Animal Hospital, Inc., Charlotte, MI

Sweers, Julie, CVT, Scott Lake Veterinary Center, Prior Lake, MN

Tallman, Renee, CVT, VCA, East Penn Animal Hospital, Emmaus, PA

Taylor, Donna, Arbor Pet Hospital, Fort Lauderdale, FL

Terry, Brandy, CVT, VTS (ECC), Animal Critical Care and Specialty Group at VRC, Malvern, PA

Thomas, Becky, Office Manager, Glenwood Falls Animal Hospital, Cypress, TX

Toale, Cyndi, Beneva Animal Hospital, Inc., Sarasota, FL

Tompkins-Rupert, Melissa, BS–Animal Science, The Cat Care Clinic, Orange, CA

Tracey, Stephen, Princeton Animal Hospital, Princeton, NJ

Trunzo, Nicholas, Arden Animal Hospital Inc., Sacramento, CA

Turk, Ron J., Practice Manager, Lyndhurst Animal Clinic, Lyndhurst, OH

Turner, Jen, Kenwood Animal Hospital, Bethesda, MD

Uba, Wendy, Hospital Administrator, Trooper Veterinary Hospital, Norristown, PA

Underwood, Jennifer, Practice Manager (not certified), Country Chase Veterinary, Tampa, FL

Wade, Victoria, Practice Manager, Bear Creek Animal Clinic, Ashland, OR

Wagaman, Judith A., CVT, North Carolina State University, College of Veterinary Medicine, Raleigh, NC

Ward, Marcy, Hudson Road Animal Hospital, Woodbury, MN

Wartalski, Martie, Practice Manager, Hoffman Estates Animal Hospital, Hoffman Estates, IL

Weaver, Bethany, Office Manager, Acres Mill Veterinary Clinic, Canton, GA

Webber, Christine, Practice Manager, Southeast Veterinary Oncology, Orange Park, FL

Wilfong, Crystal A., CVT, BS, Pets First Animal Clinic, Boise, ID

Wilkinson, Marta, CVT, West Ridge Animal Hospital, Greeley, CO

Williams, Lynn, Safe Haven Veterinary Hospital, Palm Coast, FL

Williams, Margot, CVT, Oakland Animal Hospital, Oakland, NJ

Wold, Kendra, Shiloh Veterinary Hospital, Billings, MT

Zacchio, Peggy, Breeze Animal Hospital, Panama City Beach, FL

Zirlott, Olivia, Irby-Overton Veterinary Hospital, P.C., Mobile, AL

Note: These names were copied directly from the responses the technicians provided, with changes only for obvious mistakes in names of respondents and hospitals. Also, those contributors who preferred to be anonymous are not listed here.

ABOUT THE AUTHOR

Amanda L. Donnelly, DVM, MBA, is a nationally recognized speaker and consultant who provides expertise to companion animal and specialty referral practices to help them achieve financial success within a positive, rewarding culture. She is a graduate of the College of Veterinary Medicine at the University of Missouri, Columbia, and holds an MBA from Baker University in Overland Park, Kansas, and a certificate in Veterinary Practice Administration from the AAHA Veterinary Management Institute (VMI) at Purdue University. As a second-generation veterinarian with a diverse background in small-animal practice, emergency medicine, management, and industry, she is devoted to helping veterinary practice owners and managers become better leaders and develop more effective teams. She is an active member of VetPartners and was elected to the position of vice president in 2008. Dr. Donnelly lives in central Florida with her husband, Chris Ludlow, a board-certified veterinary internist, and their dog and three cats.

Notes for tch
denl trism